Contents

G000144350

Text © Carole Creary and Gay Wilson
© 2004 Scholastic Ltd

Published by Scholastic Ltd, Villiers House,
Clarendon Avenue, Leamington Spa,
Warwickshire CV32 5PR

Printed by Bell & Bain Ltd, Glasgow

4567890 67890123

British Library Cataloguing-in-Publication Data
A catalogue record for this book is available from
the British Library.

ISBN 0-439-98492-0

Visit our website at
www.scholastic.co.uk

CD Developed in association with
Footmark Media Ltd

Authors
Carole Creary and Gay Wilson

Editor
Christine Harvey

Assistant Editors
Dulcie Booth
Jon Hill

Series Designer
Joy Monkhouse

Designer
Clare Brewer

Cover photographs
© Photodisc,
© Stockbyte,
Digital Vision

Acknowledgements

Extracts from the National Curriculum for England © Crown copyright material is reproduced with the permission of the Controller of HMSO and the Queen's Printer for Scotland.

Every effort has been made to trace copyright holders and the publishers apologise for any omissions.

Made with Macromedia is a trademark of Macromedia, Inc. Director Copyright © 1984-2000 Macromedia, Inc.

Minimum Specifications:
PC: Windows 98 SE or higher
Processor: Pentium 2 (or equivalent) 400 MHz
RAM: 128 Mb
CD-ROM drive: 48x (52x preferred)

MAC: OS 9.2 (OSX preferred)
Processor: G3 400 MHz
RAM: 128 Mb
CD-ROM drive: 48x (52x preferred)

List of resources on the CD-ROM

The page numbers refer to the teacher's notes provided in this book.

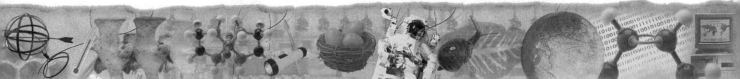

INTRODUCTION

This book and CD-ROM support the teaching and learning set out in the QCA Scheme of Work for science in Year 1. The CD provides a large bank of visual and aural resources. This book provides teacher's notes to accompany the CD resources, which contain background information, ideas for discussion and activities, along with photocopiable pages to support the teaching. All have been specifically chosen to meet the requirements for resources listed in the six QCA units for Year 1. Some additional resources and ideas have also been included to enable teachers to develop and broaden these areas of study if they wish. These include stories, simple information sheets and worksheets to help children clarify their thinking or record things they find out.

The resources and activities are not a structure for teaching in themselves, but are designed to provide a basis for discussion and activities that focus on the knowledge, skills and understanding required by the National Curriculum for science. Some of the ideas build on the National Curriculum requirements and help to broaden the children's experiences.

The children are encouraged, through using the resources on the CD and their accompanying activities, to develop such skills as observing, questioning, describing, sorting, sequencing, finding out, speaking, listening, reading, writing and drawing.

Links with other subjects
Literacy
There are a number of close links between the topics covered in this book and work on literacy. The discussion activities contribute directly to the requirements for speaking and listening. Some of the stories, poems and information sheets could be used in shared reading during the Literacy Hour, or to provide a stimulus for shared, guided or independent writing. There is considerable opportunity for the children to develop their independent writing skills as they produce leaflets or diaries, or write simple poems using the word cards. Pictures from the CD could be printed to stimulate children's independent writing or to illustrate it.

Maths
Skills such as counting, matching, ordering and sequencing are essential to both science and maths. Many of the suggested activities in this book require the children to use such skills. For example, putting the baby animal with its parent (page 11) encourages matching skills. Using plastic bricks to follow and make patterns (page 34) fosters sequencing skills. Sorting is an important mathematical and science skill and children have many opportunities to practice it in the activities here, for example when sorting materials according to different criteria (page 38).

History
In comparing the materials used in modern buildings with those used in the past (pages 34 and 35), children will begin to have an understanding of what houses were like a long time ago and how some building materials have changed over time.

Design and technology
Making a simple musical instrument from reclaimed materials (page 73) helps children to realise that design, as well as choosing the right materials, has an important part to play in terms of whether their instrument will function as well as it could.

Art and design
Many of the activities suggested in this book encourage children to use art and design to extend their understanding of a particular concept. For example, making a detailed drawing of a friend encourages close observation and an understanding of line and shape (page 12). Using clay to design and make a small object (page 39) helps children to develop their ideas in three dimensions. Collage is used to reinforce children's understanding of the properties of some materials as well as developing their feeling for texture and an aesthetic awareness of colour.

Music
In the 'Sound and hearing' chapter, children explore both listening to, and making, a variety of sounds. They can listen to and discuss music in terms of the instruments being played and how it makes them feel.

HOW TO USE THE CD-ROM

Windows NT users
If you use Windows NT you may see the following error message: 'The procedure entry point Process32First could not be located in the dynamic link library KERNEL32.dll'. Click on **OK** and the CD will autorun with no further problems.

Setting up your computer for optimal use
On opening, the CD will alert you if changes are needed in order to operate the CD at its optimal use. There are three changes you may be advised to make:

Viewing resources at their maximum screen size
To see images at their maximum screen size, your screen display needs to be set to 800 x 600 pixels. In order to adjust your screen size you will need to **Quit** the program.

If using a PC, open the **Control Panel**. Select **Display** and then **Settings**. Adjust the **Desktop Area** to 800 x 600 pixels. Click on **OK** and then restart the program.

If using a Mac, from the **Apple** menu select **Control Panels** and then **Monitors** to adjust the screen size.

Adobe Acrobat Reader
To print high-quality versions of images and to view and print the photocopiable pages on the CD you need **Adobe Acrobat Reader** installed on your computer. If you do not have it installed already, a version is provided on the CD. To install this version **Quit** the 'Ready Resources' program.

If using a PC, right-click on the **Start** menu on your desktop and choose **Explore**. Click on the + sign to the left of the CD drive entitled 'Ready Resources' and open the folder called 'Acrobat Reader Installer'. Run the program contained in this folder to install **Adobe Acrobat Reader**.

If using a Mac, double click on the 'Ready Resources' icon on the desktop and on the 'Acrobat Reader Installer' folder. Run the program contained in this folder to install **Adobe Acrobat Reader**.

PLEASE NOTE: If you do not have **Adobe Acrobat Reader** installed, you will not be able to print high-quality versions of images, or to view or print photocopiable pages (although these are provided in the accompanying book and can be photocopied).

QuickTime
In order to view the videos and listen to the audio on this CD you will need to have **QuickTime version 5 or later** installed on your computer. If you do not have it installed already or have an older version of **QuickTime**, the latest version can be downloaded at http://www.apple.com/quicktime/download/win.html. If you choose to install this version, **Quit** the 'Ready Resources' program.

PLEASE NOTE: If you do not have **QuickTime** installed you will be unable to view the films.

Menu screen
▶ Click on the **Resource Gallery** of your choice to view the resources available under that topic.
▶ Click on **Complete Resource Gallery** to view all the resources available on the CD.
▶ Click on **Photocopiable Resources (PDF format)** to view a list of the photocopiables provided in the book that accompanies this CD.
▶ **Back**: click to return to the **opening screen**. Click **Continue** to move to the **Menu screen**.
▶ **Quit**: click **Quit** to close the menu program and progress to the **Quit screen.** If you quit from the **Quit screen** you will exit the CD. If you do not quit you will return to the **Menu screen**.

Resource Galleries
▶ **Help**: click **Help** to find support on accessing and using images.
▶ **Back to menu:** click here to return to the **Menu screen**.
▶ **Quit:** click here to move to the **Quit screen** – see **Quit** above.

Viewing images

Small versions of each image are shown in the Resource Gallery. Click and drag the slider on the slide bar to scroll through the images in the Resource Gallery, or click on the arrows to move the images frame by frame. Roll the pointer over an image to see the caption.

▶ Click on an image to view the screen-sized version of it.

▶ To return to the Resource Gallery click on **Back to Resource Gallery**.

Viewing videos

Click on the video icon of your choice in the Resource Gallery. In order to view the videos on this CD, you will need to have **QuickTime** installed on your computer (see 'Setting up your computer for optimal use' above).

Once at the video screen, use the buttons on the bottom of the video screen to operate the video. The slide bar can be used for a fast forward and rewind. To return to the Resource Gallery click on **Back to Resource Gallery**.

Listening to sound recordings

Click on the required sound icon. Use the buttons or the slide bar to hear the sound. A transcript will be displayed on the viewing screen where appropriate. To return to the Resource Gallery, click on **Back to Resource Gallery**.

Printing

Click on the image to view it (see 'Viewing images' above). There are two print options:

Print using Acrobat enables you to print a high-quality version of an image. Choosing this option means that the image will open as a read-only page in **Adobe Acrobat** and in order to access these files you will need to have already installed **Adobe Acrobat Reader** on your computer (see 'Setting up your computer for optimal use' above). To print the selected resource, select **File** and then **Print**. Once you have printed the resource **minimise** or **close** the Adobe screen using — or **X** in the top right-hand corner of the screen. Return to the Resource Gallery by clicking on **Back to Resource Gallery**.

Simple print enables you to print a lower quality version of the image without the need to use **Adobe Acrobat Reader**. Select the image and click on the **Simple print** option. After printing, click on **Back to Resource Gallery**.

Slideshow presentation

If you would like to present a number of resources without having to return to the Resource Gallery and select a new image each time, you can compile a slideshow. Click on the **+** tabs at the top of each image in the Resource Gallery you would like to include in your presentation (pictures, sound and video can be included). It is important that you click on the images in the order in which you would like to view them (a number will appear on each tab to confirm the order). If you would like to change the order, click on **Clear slideshow** and begin again. Once you have selected your images – up to a maximum of 20 – click on **Play slideshow** and you will be presented with the first of your selected resources. To move to the next selection in your slideshow click on **Next slide**, to see a previous resource click on **Previous slide**. You can end your slideshow presentation at any time by clicking on **Resource Gallery**. Your slideshow selection will remain selected until you **Clear slideshow** or return to the **Menu screen**.

Viewing on an interactive whiteboard or data projector

Resources can be viewed directly from the CD. To make viewing easier for a whole class, use a large monitor, data projector or interactive whiteboard. For group, paired or individual work, the resources can be viewed from the computer screen.

Photocopiable resources (PDF format)

To view or print a photocopiable resource page, click on the required title in the list and the page will open as a read-only page in **Adobe Acrobat**. In order to access these files you will need to have already installed **Adobe Acrobat Reader** on your computer (see 'Setting up your computer for optimal use' above). To print the selected resource select **File** and then **Print**. Once you have printed the resource **minimise** or **close** the Adobe screen using — or **X** in the top right-hand corner of the screen. This will take you back to the list of PDF files. To return to the **Menu screen**, click on **Back**.

LIVING THINGS

Content and skills

This chapter links to Unit 1A 'Ourselves' and 1B 'Growing plants' of the QCA Scheme of Work for science at Key Stage 1. The units have been combined here under the title of 'Living things'. The Living Things Resource Gallery on the CD-ROM, together with the teacher's notes and photocopiable pages in this chapter, can be used when teaching the two units.

As with the QCA Scheme of Work, this chapter looks at exploring and using the senses and observing and describing living things. The resources will be useful in helping children learn about similarities and differences between living things and how to use their senses to explore the world around them. The teacher's notes suggest ways of using the resources as a whole class, for group work or with individual children. Some of the activities suggested will link with other areas of the curriculum, such as English, maths or art. Wherever possible the activities encourage the children to ask questions and develop an enquiring approach to their learning.

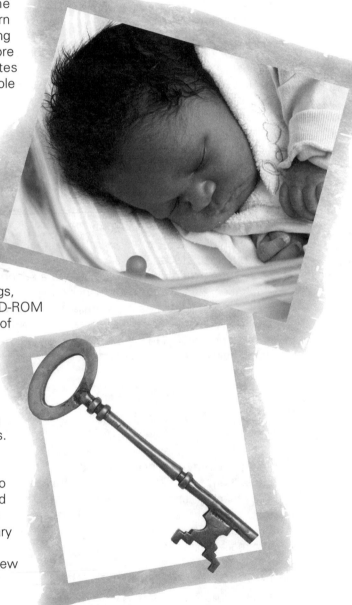

Resources on the CD-ROM

There are photographs and illustrations of animals and plants, parts of the body, animals and their young and some examples of non-living things, such as a spoon and a bucket. Also on the CD-ROM are videos of animals moving and audio clips of familiar sounds. The accompanying teacher's notes contain background information and suggest ways to use the resources when teaching the children. There are suggestions for stories and poems to be used to support the learning, some of which have been retold on the photocopiable pages.

Photocopiable pages

The photocopiable pages in the book are also provided in PDF format on the CD-ROM and can be printed from there. They include:
▶ word cards containing essential vocabulary for the topics
▶ familiar stories about living things and a new story focusing on the senses
▶ a writing frame.

Science skills

The children can learn skills such as observing, questioning, describing, sorting, sequencing, finding out, listening, speaking, reading, writing and drawing through the activities in this chapter. For example, looking closely at the series of photographs showing human growth from infancy to old age, sorting and sequencing them, will help children observe the noticeable differences that occur as humans grow and age. Discussing these differences, asking questions and listening to the ideas of others will help them to develop questioning, speaking and listening skills. Drawing family portraits and writing about them will enhance their writing, drawing and painting skills.

NOTES ON THE CD-ROM RESOURCES

Animal kingdom

This illustration shows a variety of animals likely to be found in the British Isles. Children do not always understand that humans are part of the animal kingdom, so it is important to name the human as one of the animals when looking at the drawing. They also often think that insects, fish and birds are not animals. It is important that they begin to appreciate that all creatures, large or small, belong to the animal kingdom.

Discussing the illustration

▶ Ask the children to look carefully at the illustration and tell you what they can see in it. Discuss how it shows a scene with lots of living creatures in it and point out that it includes things that live on the land, in the water and that fly in the air.
▶ Stress the fact that humans are also animals, as are all the creatures, including the insects, the fish and the birds.
▶ Talk about what the creatures are doing. For example, the cows in the field are grazing, the butterfly is flying, and so on.
▶ Ask the children which of the animals in the illustration might be pets and might live with the person on the bridge. Which of the animals do they think might need a human animal to help look after them?
▶ Ask the children to tell you about any animals they may have at home or living nearby.

Activities

▶ Ask the children to identify all the animals in the illustration and make a list on a board or flip chart as the children name them.
▶ Ask the children to name other animals that could be included in the drawing and add these to the list. Can they say what kind of place these animals might live in?
▶ Ask the children to do a drawing of a scene showing different animals from those in the illustration. Encourage them to include animals that live on the land, in water and that fly.
▶ Ask the children to draw a similar scene based in a different country using books and other secondary sources to help them research what animals would be present.
▶ Ask the children to keep a diary of any animals they see during the week. Stress that pets count only once! Which type of animal was seen most often, and which the least often?

THE HUMAN BODY

Labelled body, Unlabelled body

Children need to learn about their bodies and how they work. At this stage they need to be able to identify and locate parts of their body. Knowing about the parts of their own bodies helps them to recognise and point out the similarities and differences between themselves and other humans, and between humans and other animals. The 'Labelled body' shows the main parts of the human body with labels that the children should be familiar with from the Foundation Stage. 'Unlabelled body' is the same diagram without labels so that it can be used in a more flexible way where the children can add their own labels.

Discussing the illustrations

▶ Ask the children to tell you what they know about their own bodies. For example, can they point to and name all the main external parts?
▶ Point to the different parts of the body on the 'Labelled body' illustration and ask the children to identify the same parts on their friend's body.
▶ Do the children think that all human beings have the same body parts? Do they think that all humans' body parts work in the same way? (This may provide an opportunity to talk sensitively about people with disabilities and how they manage in their daily lives.)

Activities

▶ Play the game 'Simon says' or sing a song such as 'Heads, shoulders, knees and toes' with the children to familiarise them with their body parts.

▶ Use the 'Labelled body' illustration to remind the children of the names of familiar parts of their bodies and ask them if they can point to and name some less familiar parts, such as their tongue, chin or shin. Have some blank labels ready on which to write the children's suggestions to add to the drawing.

▶ Look at the drawing 'Labelled body' again and point to any parts that are not yet labelled. Ask the children to name these parts. Make new labels to add to the illustration (include such things as fingernails, hair, eyebrows).

▶ Use the 'Unlabelled body' illustration and ask the children to label as many parts of the body as they can. They could use some of the word cards on photocopiable page 19 to start them off, with key words such as *arm* and *leg*.

▶ Read some poems about bodies to the children, such as *Freckly Feet and Itchy Knees* by Michael Rosen (Collins) and *Poems about: Me* edited by Brian Moses (Hodder Wayland).

THE SENSES

Ear, Eyes, Nose, Tongue, Hand

Children need to understand that they use their senses to explore and make sense of the world around them. They need to be able to name their senses and know which sense organ is associated with each one. They also need to know that sight, hearing, taste, smell and touch are together called our senses. Talking about the senses may be an opportunity to discuss with the children that some people may have visual, auditory and other sensory impairments. Remind the children that although the senses are necessary to tell us about our surroundings and to help keep us safe, they also give us great pleasure.

Discussing the photograph of the ear
▶ Look at the photograph of the ear and ask the children to point to their own ears.
Ask, *What do we use our ears for?*
▶ Ask the children to cover one ear. Can they still hear you talking?
▶ Ask them to cover both ears. Can they hear you now?

Discussing the photograph of the eyes
▶ Look at the photograph of the eyes and ask the children to point to their own. Are the children's eyes the same colour as those in the photograph?
▶ Ask them to look at their friend's eyes. Do they have the same coloured eyes?
▶ Ask a child to look out of the classroom window and describe what they can see.
▶ Ask why the children think our sense of sight is important. Talk about how we can see where we are going so that we don't fall down stairs or walk into things, for example.

Discussing the photograph of the nose
▶ Look with the children at the photograph and ask them to point to their own nose.
▶ Ask the children to name their favourite smell and to tell everyone why they like it.
▶ Why do the children think our sense of smell is important? For example, it helps us to taste things and it can help to keep us safe (we can smell gas or rotten food that may be harmful).

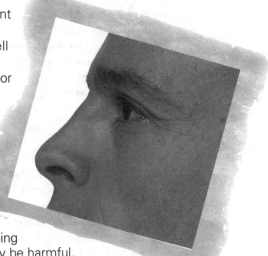

Discussing the photograph of the tongue
▶ Look at the photograph of the tongue and ask the children to locate their own.
▶ In pairs, ask the children to look at each other's tongues (magnifying lenses would be useful). What can they see? Explain that all the little bumps help us to taste things.
▶ Ask why our sense of taste is important. For example, in keeping us safe by warning us that if something tastes *that* nasty it may be harmful.

Discussing the photograph of the hand
▶ Look at the hand in this photograph. Discuss with the children how it shows the finger pads and explain that these are particularly sensitive to touch.

▶ Explain to the children that the skin on the whole of our bodies is sensitive to touch, not just the fingertips.

▶ Talk about how the sense of touch helps us to locate things and how being able to feel pain warns us that a part of our body is in danger or has been damaged.

Activities

▶ Use the word cards on photocopiable pages 17 and 18 to familiarise the children with the key words, such as *ear*, *nose*, *taste*.

▶ Read the story 'The princess and the pea' (photocopiable page 26) and discuss how the princess was so sensitive to touch she could even feel a tiny pea through layers of mattresses.

▶ In pairs, ask the children to face each other and touch fingertips. Now ask them to close their eyes tightly. Can they find their partner's fingertips as easily? How do their eyes help them?

▶ Working in pairs, ask the children to take it in turns to close their eyes while their partner touches them gently. Can they tell their partner which part of them is being touched?

▶ Ask some children to share a pleasurable experience that they have had and describe the part their senses played in it. For example, listening to music, eating their favourite meal, stroking their cat.

▶ Discuss how some people with visual impairment use the sense of touch in their fingertips to read Braille, which is an alphabet made up of different patterns of raised dots. A sample of Braille for the children to feel would be useful.

▶ Play the children the 'Familiar sounds' (provided in the Living Things Resource Gallery on the CD) and ask the children to listen carefully and identify them.

▶ Read the story of 'Little Red Riding Hood' (photocopiable page 28) with the children to reinforce the relationship between a sense organ and the sense for which it is used.

▶ Read the story 'Bored!' (photocopiable page 24) to the children and ask them to point to the appropriate part of their body as a sense is mentioned. For example, they should point to their nose at the smell of baking, or wriggle their fingers when they hear about touch.

GROWING

Human baby, Toddler, Children, Teenager, Middle-aged adult, Elderly person

This series of photographs shows how humans grow and age irrespective of race or gender. Children need to know that there are sequential stages in life for all human beings and these photographs show images representative of the main stages.

Discussing the photographs

▶ Show the children all the photographs in age sequence. Discuss the main stages of human growth and development as represented in the photographs.

▶ Can the children tell you which stages they have been through themselves and where they think they are now? What is the next stage they will reach?

▶ Some children may be sensitive about their height or the size of their feet. Discuss the fact that we grow and develop at different rates and that the oldest child in the class may not necessarily be the tallest. Point out that even when fully grown we are still all different. For example, are all the adults in the school the same height? Do they all have the same sized feet?

Activities

▶ Read the poem 'When I was One' by AA Milne from *Now We Are Six* (Methuen Young Books) to reinforce the idea that human beings pass through stages as they grow.

▶ Ask the children to put the photographs in order from youngest to oldest.

▶ Look carefully at the photographs and describe the main changes between each stage of development. For example, the difference in height, change in shape of face, body, limbs. Ask the children how the teenager and middle-aged adult are different from the baby and the elderly person. Get them to focus on things like how hair changes, including colour and amount.

▶ Ask the children for examples of any differences between themselves and younger members of their family and list these. For example, the need to have a nappy changed or to be fed. Ask the children to add anything else that they have noticed about older members of their family that are different from the things they need, such as the need for a hearing aid.

▶ Put the class in a line in age order and ask *Is the oldest the tallest? Is the youngest the shortest?* Let the children use the word cards on photocopiable page 21 to help them write sentences about their observations, using words such as *taller, tallest, different from.*

ANIMALS AND THEIR YOUNG

Adult human, Human baby, Duck, Duckling, Sheep, Lamb, Butterfly, Caterpillar, Elephant, Elephant calf

This selection of adult and baby animal photographs includes some where the baby looks like a miniature of the adult from birth, for example the humans and elephants. Others, such as the butterfly, have young that look very different from the adult and go through major changes as they grow. While the duckling is recognisable as a bird it does not look very much like an adult duck at birth. Children need to know that all animals reproduce, but not all babies look like their corresponding adult.

Discussing the photographs

▶ Show the children the photograph of the 'Human baby'. Discuss with them how they can tell immediately that a human baby is human and not, for example, a lamb. Note with them that the baby has a human face and two arms. The hands are smaller versions of those of an adult human. Its skin is smooth and not covered by wool like a lamb's.

▶ Talk about other babies that look like miniatures of the adult. Look at the photographs of the 'Elephant' and 'Elephant calf' and of the 'Sheep' and 'Lamb'.

▶ Do the children know any babies that are completely different from the adult? Look at the 'Caterpillar' and 'Butterfly' photographs to illustrate this point.

▶ Look at the photographs of the 'Duck' and the 'Duckling'. Ask, *How similar is the duckling to the adult duck?*

Activities

▶ Use all the photographs together and ask the children to match the baby animal to its parent. Discuss how they knew which ones to put together.

▶ Ask the children to name all the animals. Ask them if they know the proper name for each baby (*elephant calf*, rather than *baby elephant*).

▶ Use the word cards on photocopiable page 19 for the children to add labels to the photographs, applying words such as *hoof, wing, beak* to the animals.

▶ Ask the children to say how the humans are different from the other animals in the photographs. For example, humans walk upright on two legs while most animals walk on more – dogs and cats walk on four, insects have six, spiders have eight, and so on.

▶ Look at the photographs and ask the children to draw or list features that humans do not have but the other animals have. For example, feathers, tails or wings.

Same but different children

Children need to understand that although humans all look different we are all human beings and, therefore, are all essentially the same. They need to know that there are differences within ethnic groups as well as between ethnic groups, for example in hair or eye colour, skin tone, build. Make sure that the children concentrate on real similarities and differences and do not include things like hairstyle or colour of clothes. This photograph shows children of the same age but of different build, height, hair colour, ethnicity and gender.

Discussing the photograph

▶ Ask the children to describe to you what they see in the photograph.

▶ How many similarities can they see between the children in the photograph? For example, each has two eyes, two arms, two legs, and so on. Ask them what the main thing they all have in common is (that they are human beings).

▶ Ask the children to tell you as many differences as they can see. For example, skin colour, hair colour, eye colour, height, and so on.

Activities
▶ Make a list, either in words or pictures, of all the similarities the children identified. Make a similar list of all the differences. Compare the lists. Are there more similarities or differences between the children in the photograph?
▶ Ask the children to look carefully at each other. What similarities and differences are there? In pairs, ask the children to draw these.

LIVING AND NON-LIVING

Metal tin, Key, Spoon, Bucket, Woodlouse, Snail, Stone

Children at this stage may have difficulty in differentiating between things that are living and non-living. They need to understand that living things grow, move, feed and use their senses. These photographs show things that are obviously living or non-living. At a later stage children will need to be able to distinguish between things that are living, non-living and that have never been alive. For example, a tree, things made from wood, and a stone.

Discussing the photographs
▶ Show the children each photograph in turn. Ask them to identify the object in each of them.
▶ Discuss which are living and which are non-living and ask the children how they know. For example, the snail and woodlouse can move but the stone and metal tin cannot.

Activities
▶ Ask the children to sort the photographs into groups of living and non-living things. Can they tell you how they knew which groups to put the photographs in and give as many reasons as possible?
▶ Take the children into the playground and make lists of the living and non-living things they can see. Remind them that plants are living things too.
▶ Put out a collection of living and non-living things, such as fruit and vegetables (cut in half or lengths), plastic cotton reels, plastic shapes or cutters, stones, and so on. Ask the children to sort them into groups and use them to make prints of living and non-living things.
▶ Let the children use the word cards on photocopiable page 20 to label the collection of objects with words such as *living*, *non-living*, *alive*.

VIDEO: ANIMALS MOVING

Horses galloping, Bird flying, Perch swimming, Hares hopping, Cheetah running, Snail moving, Butterfly flying

These video clips will enable children to observe, in detail, a variety of animals moving. Children often take the fact that animals move for granted, without considering exactly how they move and which parts of the body are involved. Snails may be kept in a plastic tank for a short time so that the children can observe the way they move at close quarters. If the children are patient they can feel the snails move across their hands. Remind the children to treat all living things with care and sensitivity, and to make sure they wash their hands after handling animals.

Discussing the video
▶ Before showing the video clips, tell the children that they need to look carefully because you are going to ask questions about how each animal moves and which part of their bodies they use afterwards.
▶ Show each animal moving, one at a time. Ask the children if they can name the animal. Then ask which parts of the body each animal used when moving. Notice the strong back legs of the hare that it uses to push off from the ground. Similarly, the horse and cheetah use their legs to push and pull themselves along. The pigeon and the butterfly use their wings to pull them through the air. The snail has no arms, legs or wings but it does have a foot! The strong muscle on its underside contracts and relaxes to pull it along at 'a snail's pace'. The fish uses its tail to propel it through the water. Its fins are mainly there to guide it.
▶ Compare each animal moving with the way humans move. Do they use the same or different body parts?

Activities

▶ In PE, reinforce what the children have learned by asking them to mimic the different animal movements.

▶ Use the photographs from 'Animals and their young' (provided in the Living Things Resource Gallery) for the children to group animals that move in similar ways.

▶ Let the children use simple reference books to research how other animals move and which parts of their bodies they use.

FAMILIAR SOUNDS

Doorbell, Vacuum cleaner, Owl, Baby crying

These audio clips contain familiar sounds for the children to identify. You may need to play them more than once. Children need to know that they hear sounds by listening with their ears. These sensitive organs send messages to the brain so that sounds can be distinguished. The sense of hearing helps us to communicate and make sense of the world around us, and identifying warning sounds can help to keep us safe.

Discussing the sounds

▶ Tell the children you are going to play a series of sounds and ask them to point to the sense organ they use to listen with.

▶ Play the sounds and ask the children how many different sounds they heard.

▶ Do the children recognise any of the sounds?

▶ Discuss with the children the importance of the sense of hearing and how we need to care for it by avoiding continuous loud noises. This may be an opportunity to discuss, sensitively, people who have a hearing impairment.

▶ Ask the children to cover their ears while you play the clips again. Can they hear now?

Activities

▶ In pairs, give one child a short message and ask them to tell their partner by using their lips but without making a sound. Can their partner lip-read the message? If the child relaying the message turns away from their partner, can the message still be understood?

▶ Set a tape recorder running at some point during the day, such as when the children are clearing up. Play the tape back and ask the children if they can tell you what is happening.

▶ Ask a child to come out and stand with its back to the class. Point to one or two children and ask them to speak. Can the child with its back to the class identify the speakers?

Interview: Pet care

It is important for children to know that all living things should be treated with care and respect. They need to understand that pets are a responsibility as well as a pleasure, because they depend on their owners for all their needs. This video shows a dog owner talking about how she looks after her pet Labrador called Webster.

Discussing the interview

▶ Before playing the interview to the children, ask them to tell you if they have a pet at home and who looks after it.

▶ Ask them to tell you some of the things that pets need to keep them healthy and contented.

▶ Tell them that they are going to listen to someone talking about caring for a pet. Ask them to listen and watch carefully to see if this person's pet has the same needs as the pets they have talked about.

▶ Once the children have seen the video ask them to tell you what sort of pet is being talked about. Can they remember the dog's name? (Webster.)

▶ Ask, *What does it like to eat? How many times a day is it fed?*

▶ Ask, *What does it drink? Can it get a drink at any time? Where is its water kept?*

▶ Ask, *How does it get its exercise? Does it have to be taken for walks?*

▶ Can the children remember if the dog lives in a special place?

▶ What happens to the dog if it gets ill?

▶ How long will the dog live for?

▶ Can they remember if it has toys or playthings?

Activities
▶ Bring in a collection of pet care leaflets for the children to see. Can they find a leaflet about their own or their friend's pet? Do all pets need to be looked after in the same way?
▶ As individuals, or in small groups, ask the children to choose an animal and to produce a pet care leaflet for it using words and pictures. They could use the 'Taking care of my pet' (photocopiable page 32) format.
▶ Borrow a pet for a short time and let the children care for it. Make a list of all its needs.
▶ Visit a pet shop with the children and look at the wide variety of things that are available for pet care.

PLANTS

Tomato plants, Sweetcorn, Cabbage, Sunflower

Children need to begin to appreciate the important part that plants play in our lives and that we use them in all sorts of ways. Some children may not realise that many of the foods we buy in the supermarket are plants or parts of plants. Some children fail to recognise trees as plants. It is useful to have a collection of pot plants in the classroom when teaching this unit.

Discussing the photographs
▶ Talk to the children about the need to care for living things, including wild flowers and trees.
▶ Encourage the children to think about their environment and their role in caring for it. Ask why they think plants are important. Explain that they are an important source of food. They also help to provide a pleasant environment.
▶ Show the children the photographs and ask if they recognise any of them. Can they tell you what food we get from each plant?
▶ Discuss which part of the plants we eat. For example, the fruit from the tomatoes, the seeds from the sunflowers and sweetcorn, and the leaves from the cabbage.

Activities
▶ Take the children outside and look for any plants around the school, asking the children to describe them. For example, *Trees are tall, have thick branches and lots of leaves* (depending on the season); *Grass grows all over the playing field and in the cracks between stones.*
▶ Use the photograph of the sunflower and ask the children to point to and name different parts of the plant, such as the flower, a leaf and the stem.
▶ Create a class collage or picture showing the variety of plant life the children can think of.
▶ Read 'The enormous turnip' (photocopiable page 30) and encourage the children to act out the story.
▶ Make a simple snack using plants for the children to try, such as a vegetable or fruit salad, or vegetable soup.
▶ Stories such as *Jasper's Beanstalk* by Nick Butterworth and Mick Inkpen (Hodder Children's Books) or *The Trouble with Grandad* by Babette Cole (Methuen Young Books) are useful in introducing or reinforcing the ideas in this unit.

Pot bound plant

Children may be familiar with the parts of a plant they see above ground, but may not realise that plants have roots and that these are a very important part of the plant. Plants need to have room for their roots to grow and develop in order to keep them healthy. When a plant has become pot bound it means that the roots are filling the pot and there is no room for them to grow further. Some roots may be seen coming through the bottom of the pot. Unless the plant is re-potted into a bigger pot it could fail to thrive and may eventually die. Plants can be taken from pots and replaced without damage if the roots are not disturbed too much.

Discussing the photograph
▶ Look at the photograph with the children. Get them to name and talk about the different parts of the plant they can see.

▶ Ask the children to look carefully at the roots. Discuss the fact that a plant needs a healthy root system to keep it stable and to take up water.

▶ Ask the children why they think that the plant in the photograph needs re-potting (because the roots have become too big for its pot).

Activities

▶ Compare the roots of the plant in the photograph with the roots of any other pot plants you have in the classroom. Are they the same colour? Are they as thick? Are there as many?

▶ Ask the children to draw pictures of plants showing the main parts, particularly the roots.

▶ Rest hyacinth bulbs or onions on the rims of clear containers filled with water and let the children watch the roots develop.

▶ Take the children outside and look to see if any of the trees have some of their roots visible above ground.

NOTES ON THE PHOTOCOPIABLE PAGES

Word cards PAGE 17

These word cards contain some of the basic vocabulary for the children to use and learn when looking at the QCA units 'Ourselves' and 'Growing plants'. They include:

▶ words relating to the senses

▶ words relating to the parts of the body

▶ words relating to living and non-living

▶ words to enable comparisons to be made

▶ words relating to plants.

Read through the word cards with the children to familiarise them with the key words of the unit. Ask which words the children have heard before, clarifying any they don't understand.

Activities

▶ Cut a number of the words out and spread them on the table. Ask the children to find specific words.

▶ Use the words as a word bank to help the children label pictures or to help them with their writing.

Bored! PAGE 24

Use this story to reinforce the children's knowledge of which sense goes with which organ.

Discussing the story

▶ Remind the children about which sense organ we use for each sense. Talk about the importance of senses and how they help to tell us about the world we live in.

Activities

▶ As each smell, sight, touch, sound or taste is mentioned, ask the children to point to the appropriate sense organ.

▶ Ask the children to think about a pleasurable experience they have had associated with one of their senses, and to write a few words or a poem about it.

▶ Ask the children to draw a cartoon strip of someone using each sense, for example someone smelling a flower. Get them to label the pictures with the sense being used.

The princess and the pea PAGE 26

Perhaps one of the less familiar fairy stories, it illustrates the sense of touch and feeling well. It tells how the princess was able to feel a pea through layers and layers of mattresses.

Discussing the story

▶ Tell the children the story for enjoyment and relaxation.

▶ Talk about how uncomfortable the princess must have been if she could feel the pea through all those mattresses. Remind the children how sensitive our sense of touch can be.

► Talk about how we often feel things with our fingers but that we can, in fact, feel with every part of our bodies.

► Ask the children if they have ever had to sit or lie on anything that felt really uncomfortable, such as a pebbly beach.

Activities

► The children could investigate how many layers of fabric they can feel a pea through. Place a dried pea on a table and gradually add layers of fabric until it is impossible to feel the pea with the fingertips.

► Place a small object under several layers of fabric and ask the children to find out what it is by using their sense of touch.

Little Red Riding Hood

PAGE 28

This familiar story mentions just about all of the senses and sense organs.

Discussing the story

► Discuss with the children whether they think that bigger eyes or ears really mean that you can see or hear better.

► Talk about why some animals have bigger sensory organs and why some can move them. For example, dogs can pinpoint sounds by moving their ears and owls have big eyes to collect more light to help them hunt at night. Ask the children if they can move their ears.

Activities

► Make a large class collage of the wolf in Grandma's bed and label it with captions such as *All the better to see you with*, *All the better to eat you with*, linked to the correct sense organ.

► Make a collection of materials and objects that relate to each of the senses. For example, bells, samples of rough and smooth materials, sweet wrappers and boxes, perfume bottles, herb and spice packets, spectacles, sunglasses, photographs or picture books. Ask the children to sort them according to which sense they are associated with.

The enormous turnip

PAGE 30

Children can join in the repetitions or help to act out this story. Many small children believe that food originates in the local supermarket and they do not appreciate that vegetables and fruits have been grown in a field or greenhouse and that they have been harvested by the farmers before being packed and transported to the shops. This story can be a starting point towards them understanding that vegetables, such as a turnip, grow in the ground.

Discussing the story

► Help children to understand that some of our food actually grows in the ground and needs to be harvested before we can eat it.

► Discuss how farmers these days often use machines to harvest or dig up the crops instead of having to pull things up by hand, but that people who grow things in their gardens or allotments still have to dig or pull things up in this way.

Activities

► Provide enough pieces of turnip for each child to feel and smell. Cook some turnip and allow each child to taste a little.

► If you have a school garden, let the children try weeding a patch to see how difficult it is to pull some things up.

► Let the children use seed catalogues to find out about other vegetables that need pulling out of the soil so that the root can be eaten.

Taking care of my pet

PAGE 32

This photocopiable can be used for the children to make their own leaflet about how to care for a pet. Fold the A4 sheet in half, leaving the front and back of the page for the children to draw the front of their pet on the front and the back of their pet on the back!

Senses word cards (1)

sense
eye
sight
see
ear
hearing

Senses word cards (2)

nose

smell

tongue

taste

touch

feel

Parts of the body word cards

arm

leg

wing

head

beak

hoof

Living and non-living word cards

alive

living

not alive

non-living

human

animal

Comparing word cards

tall

taller

tallest

like

similar to

different from

branch

flower

root

stem

leaf

Plants word cards (2)

plants

seeds

seedlings

weed

pot-bound

Bored!

Susie was fed up. She was so bored. It was Saturday and she wanted to go out in the garden and play on her swing, but it was raining. It looked as though it had been raining all night. There were puddles everywhere and the rain was still pounding down. She could hear it clattering down on the plastic roof of the lean-to and she could see big drops running down the windowpane. There was no chance of going out while it was like this.

There was a smell of baking coming from the kitchen and Susie thought that might be worth investigating. She knew Mum was busy getting ready for visitors. At least that was something to look forward to. Her cousins Jodie and Tim would be here for tea, but that was ages yet. Dad had gone to the shops. Susie often went with him, but he said it was too wet today and there was no point in two of them getting wet through. Susie idly put her hand into her pocket and felt something sticky. It was the sweet she hadn't quite finished yesterday. She pulled it out. It wasn't too fluffy so she popped it in her mouth to finish it. It tasted all right. Orange was her favourite. She wasn't so keen on the green ones, but then her Dad pinched all those because they were his favourite.

Susie looked out of the window. It was still raining. Perhaps she should finish the jigsaw she had started. There were only a few pieces left to put in and that would be a surprise for Dad when he got back from shopping. She lay down on her tummy and looked under the settee where she always kept jigsaws until she had finished them. She felt the edge of the board with her fingers and carefully pulled it out. It was a picture of a big teddy bear and she only had to finish part of his ear, a bit of a foot and one eye. She found the bit for his eye quite quickly, but the pieces of ear and foot looked very much the same to Susie so she decided to wait until Mum or Dad could help. In any case, her fingers felt quite sticky from the sweet she had found and she was sticking to the jigsaw pieces. Perhaps she should go and wash her hands.

Mum had put some new soap in the bathroom. It smelled lovely, but felt very slippery, and you had to be careful that it didn't shoot all over the bathroom if you squeezed a little too hard. Susie washed her hands and dried them on the towel, which sort of felt soft and rough at the same time. As she came out of the bathroom she could hear the food mixer whirring downstairs in the kitchen. That meant cake for tea and Susie wondered if it would be her favourite – chocolate with icing on top. She liked the taste of the hundreds and thousands that Mum sometimes sprinkled all over it.

Susie was just thinking about going to her room to listen to one of her tapes when she heard a car toot. Dad was back from the shops. He always gave a little toot when he arrived, just to let them know he was back safe and sound. Susie hurried downstairs and opened the front door. She was tall enough to reach the latch now and she just managed to open the door in time to see Dad coming up the path with a box full of shopping.

"Bless you, Susie," said Dad. "I should have got wet through sorting out my keys to open the door. It's a good job you heard me."

Dad took the shopping through to the kitchen, closely followed by Susie who was anxious to see if there was anything for her in the box. Mum and Dad unpacked the box and put the things away. Sure enough, down at the bottom, was a packet of sweets.

"They are for you to share with Tim and Jodie when they get here," said Dad. "I'll leave them on the shelf here until they come. I shouldn't think they'll be long now. Go and watch for them from the front window."

Susie went and stood on her little stool so that she could see through the window and look down the road to the corner. She could see raindrops chasing each other down the pane. There were so many raindrops that it was difficult to see through them, but she could just see the lights on the cars as they went up the street and she could even hear some of them as they splashed through the puddles. At last she saw a pair of headlamps slow down and pull into the kerb next to Dad's car. She could hear the car doors slam as her uncle and auntie, Tim and Jodie hurried up the path to get out of the rain.

"Hooray," thought Susie, "someone to play with at last. It doesn't matter now if it rains all day, I shan't be bored with Tim and Jodie to play with. Now, where are those sweets? Bags I the orange one."

The princess and the pea

Once upon a time there was a handsome prince. He lived in a huge, draughty castle with his mother and father, the King and Queen. The Prince had been to school and done well at university. He had learned to ride and play tennis. He could ski and swim and he loved making things. The King and Queen decided that it was time he got married. Because he was a prince, the King and Queen said that the only suitable wife must be a princess. The problem was to find a real, genuine princess.

The Prince had lots of friends and some of them were girls that he quite liked, but none of them was a princess. Anyway, he wasn't sure that he wanted to get married yet, he was having too much fun with all his friends. But the King and Queen insisted. So the Prince set out to travel into the next kingdom to find a real princess. Unfortunately, the King and Queen of this country only had sons – not a princess in sight! So the Prince journeyed on to the next country. He met several beautiful girls, some of whom said they were princesses, but the Prince had his doubts. There was something not quite right about each of them and he couldn't be sure that any of them were real princesses. Anyway, he didn't meet one that he would like to marry even if she was a real princess!

At last the Prince decided to give up his search and return home. He was quite sad because by now he had grown quite used to the idea of getting married and having a wife and was disappointed that he hadn't found one.

One night, not long after the Prince had returned home, there was a terrible storm. The wind blew hard enough to blow down a tree in the palace garden. The rain came down in sheets and the thunder was so loud that the palace cat went and hid under the stairs. Streaks of lightning lit up the whole room. Suddenly they heard a frantic knocking at the front door.

"Surely no one is out on a night like this," said the Queen. "Whoever it is must be soaked to the skin."

"Dear, dear," said the King. "I'll go and see."

So the King himself went to open the palace door. There on the doorstep stood a young girl. She was wet through. Her hair hung down in dripping strands. Her dress clung to her legs and was splashed and stained with mud. Her dainty shoes squelched each time she moved her foot.

"Come in, come in," said the King. "It's not fit for anyone to be out on a night like this."

READY RESOURCES ▶▶ S C I E N C E

The Prince, who had been reading, looked up as the girl came in. She stood in the hall with the water streaming from her clothes and collecting in a puddle round her feet. Wet and bedraggled as she was, the Prince thought how beautiful she looked. Her face lit up with a lovely smile as she thanked the King and explained that she was a princess but had been separated from the rest of her party in the storm.

The Prince pricked up his ears when he heard this, but the Queen was not so sure. Anybody could knock at the door and say they were a princess. She had a plan to find out if this young lady really was what she claimed to be.

"Come with me, my dear," she said. "We must get you out of those wet things and you must stay the night until the storm has passed."

While the girl was getting out of her wet things and soaking in a nice hot bath, the Queen went to get a bedroom ready for her. She took with her three small, dried peas. She placed these on the bed, then she had twenty mattresses placed on top of them, and then twenty feather beds on top of the mattresses. The poor girl needed a step ladder to get into bed!

The next morning at breakfast the Prince was up early for once! The Queen asked the young lady if she had slept well.

"Thank you, but no, not really. There was something hard in the bed and I'm black and blue all over. It was very uncomfortable."

Then the Queen knew that the young lady was indeed a real princess, for surely only a real princess would have such a delicate sense of feeling that she could feel the peas through all those mattresses. The Prince was very pleased to hear this and thought that maybe he had found his bride right on his own doorstep.

Little Red Riding Hood

Once upon a time, long ago, there was a girl called Little Red Riding Hood. She lived with her mother and father on the edge of a big forest. Her father was a woodcutter and spent most of his days in the woods, cutting down trees with his axe. As well as looking after her and her father, Little Red Riding Hood's mother had to help Granny who was very old. Granny lived on the other side of the forest in a tiny cottage just big enough for one. When Little Red Riding Hood's mother did the cooking or baked cakes or did the washing, she cooked and washed for Granny too. Granny was very fond of Mother's cooking, especially her delicious cakes. Every day, Little Red Riding Hood was sent on an errand to Granny's cottage to take Granny's dinner and often some lovely cakes or biscuits for Granny in her basket.

She knew the path through the forest very well and usually skipped along so that she would be able to spend some time with her granny before it was time to go home. Sometimes, though, when it was a beautiful day, she went more slowly and enjoyed the warm sun dappling through the leaves onto the path. She watched the butterflies moving from wild flower to wild flower, sipping the nectar and moving their bright wings. She heard the birds calling and smelled the lovely smell of the woods. She knew, though, that her mother did not like her to dawdle because there was supposed to be a wolf in the woods. Granny was always pleased to see her and when she arrived they shared some of the cakes and talked about so many things. Granny was full of stories about what things were like when she was a little girl and Little Red Riding Hood loved to listen to her.

One day Mother said, "I've baked some special cakes today, the ones that Granny likes best. Her washing is ready too and you know how she misses

her best shawl when it is being washed." Mother packed Little Red Riding Hood's basket, putting the precious shawl at the bottom and then the special cakes on top, wrapped in a bright, clean cloth. Little Red Riding Hood put on her warm, red cape with the lovely soft hood and, kissing her mother goodbye, set off for Granny's house. It was a glorious day when she set out and she went more slowly than usual, enjoying the sunshine. When she was nearly halfway there, big, dark clouds began to pile up in the sky and cover the sun. Suddenly the wood seemed shadowy and a cold breeze wound through the trees.

Little Red Riding Hood shivered and began to hurry. She wished that she was at Granny's house, because the woods seemed dark and less friendly and comfortable than usual, and she felt as if someone was watching her.

It seemed odd, too, that when she arrived Granny's door was not shut. Granny was always careful about keeping her door shut. Little Red Riding Hood knocked timidly.

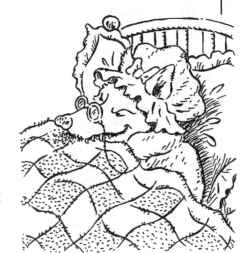

"Come in" said a deep, gruff, snarling voice, not at all like Granny's usual voice.

Little Red Riding Hood opened the door slowly and went in. There was Granny sitting up in bed with a lacy cap on her head, wearing her second best shawl and with the counterpane pulled right up to her chin. But, oh dear, she did look strange and much darker and more hairy than usual.

"Granny, what big ears you have," said Little Red Riding Hood in a small, shaky voice.

"All the better to hear you with, my dear," said the snarling voice, sounding less and less like Granny.

"What big eyes you have," said Little Red Riding Hood.

"All the better to see you with, my dear," said the person in the bed, staring at Little Red Riding Hood so hard that she shrank back against the wall.

"Granny, what a big, wet nose you have."

The person in the bed gave a noisy sniff and replied, "All the better to smell you with, my dear." Little Red Riding Hood began to edge back towards the door, ready to run.

"Oh Granny, what big teeth you have," she said.

"All the better to eat you with," the person in the bed said, licking his lips with a big red tongue.

"What a big red tongue you've got."

"All the better to taste you with," growled the person in the bed, leaping out at Little Red Riding Hood with his big teeth snapping and his red tongue lolling out of his mouth. Just as Little Red Riding Hood realised that this was not her Granny at all but the big, hairy wolf wanting to gobble her up, her father burst through the door and rescued Little Red Riding Hood.

Just then, both Little Red Riding Hood and her father heard faint noises from the cupboard under the stairs and there they found Granny, tied up. Little Red Riding Hood and her father helped her out, gave her back her best shawl and shared the special cakes.

The enormous turnip

Once upon a time there was a little old man and a little old woman. They lived happily together in a cottage on the edge of the village. The old man loved to work in his garden growing flowers, which they both loved to look at, and vegetables, which they loved to eat. The old lady was always very pleased when her husband announced: "I'm just going down the garden to see what I can find. I think the peas are just about ready," or, "There's a good cabbage that needs cutting." While he was out his wife would get out her cookery books and decide what she would do with the things her husband gathered from the garden.

One day the old man went off into the garden to see what was ready. He hadn't been gone long before he came back to ask for his wife's help.

"There's a lovely big turnip that will do nicely for our dinner, but I'm having trouble pulling it out of the ground," the little old man told his wife.

Together they went down to the garden and there, sure enough, was the biggest turnip the old lady had ever seen. The little old man caught hold of the turnip's leaves, and the little old woman got hold of her husband round his middle, and together they pulled. They pulled and they pulled, but the turnip refused to move.

Next door to the little old man and the little old woman lived a little boy and his sister. They often leaned over the fence to talk to the little old man as he worked in the garden. So the little old man called over the fence and asked the boy to come and help to pull up the turnip. When he arrived the little old man again grasped the turnip, the little old woman held him round his middle, and the boy held the little old woman round her middle, and together they all pulled as hard as they could. They pulled and they pulled, but again the turnip refused to budge. The boy said that he would go and fetch his sister so that she could help.

Again the little old man grasped the turnip. The little old woman held him round his middle and the boy held the little old woman round her middle. The little girl grasped her brother round his middle and together they all pulled as hard as they could. They pulled and they pulled and they pulled, but still the turnip refused to come out of the ground.

The boy and his sister had a dog that had followed them round into the garden.

"Our dog is very clever," said the boy. "He can help us pull and perhaps that will make a difference."

So the little old man once more took hold of the turnip. The little old woman held him round his middle and the boy held the little old woman round her middle. The little girl grasped her brother round his middle and the dog grasped the little girl's skirt in his mouth. Together they all pulled as hard as they could. They pulled and they pulled and they pulled, but still the turnip stayed firmly in the ground. The little old man took off his cap and scratched his head and wondered what to do next.

All this time the cat that lived next door had been sitting on the fence, watching. He jumped down and walked over to the little group.

"My cat will help," said the little girl.

They all got ready to pull again. The little old man took hold of the turnip. The little old woman took hold of him round his middle. The boy held the little old woman round her middle. The little girl grasped her brother round his middle and the dog grasped the little girl's skirt in his mouth. The cat carefully took hold of the dog's tail and together they all pulled. They pulled and they pulled and they pulled, but still the turnip refused to move one tiny bit.

While sitting on the fence, as well as watching the antics of the turnip pullers, the cat had also been watching a tiny mouse that had been playing near the woodpile. The cat called to the mouse and promised not to chase it if it would come and help with the turnip. "Not that it will do much good," he thought to himself.

But the mouse agreed and came over to help. So the little old man once more took hold of the turnip. The little old woman took hold of him round his middle. The boy held the little old woman round her middle. The little girl grasped her brother round his middle and the dog held the little girl's skirt in his mouth. The cat carefully took hold of the dog's tail. The mouse took hold of the cat's tail and together they all pulled.

They pulled and they pulled and they pulled and they pulled, and this time the turnip creaked and groaned and then shot out of the ground so suddenly that all those pulling fell flat on their backs. The little old man fell on top of the little old woman. The little old woman fell on top of the boy. The boy fell on top of his sister. The little girl fell on top of the dog. The dog fell on top of the cat and the cat fell on top of the mouse, who let out a very loud squeak.

When they all managed to get up again, there in front of them was the most enormous turnip any of them had ever seen. The little old man fetched his wheelbarrow and together they all heaved the turnip into it and took it back up the garden to the cottage. There the little old woman cut it up and made it into a stew that fed them all for a whole week.

Taking care of my pet

My pet is a _____

Its name is _____

Write or draw pictures in the boxes to show how to take care of your pet.

Food and drink	Grooming

Exercise	Keeping its home clean

Health care

SORTING AND USING MATERIALS

Content and skills

This chapter links to Unit 1C 'Sorting and using materials' of the QCA Scheme of Work for science at Key Stage 1. The Sorting and Using Materials Resource Gallery on the CD-ROM, together with the teacher's notes and photocopiable pages in this chapter, can be used in teaching this unit.

This chapter looks at a variety of materials and explores some of their properties. Children need to understand that materials are chosen for particular purposes because of their properties; that we use glass in windows because it is transparent, that wood can be shaped and joined which makes it suitable for furniture or building.

The teacher's notes include ideas for using the resources as a whole class, for group work or as individuals. Some of the activities suggested will link with other areas of the curriculum, such as English, maths or art. Wherever possible the activities encourage the children to ask questions and develop an enquiring approach to their learning.

© Paul Rogers/Pellier 07974 147665

Resources on the CD-ROM

Children obviously need to handle and feel materials in a practical way, but the resources on the CD-ROM can be used to reinforce and enhance the children's learning. Teacher's notes accompany every resource, and these contain background information about the resource as well as suggesting ways to use it in teaching.

Photocopiable pages

The photocopiable pages in the book are also provided in PDF format on the CD-ROM and can be printed from there. They include:
▶ word cards containing essential vocabulary for the topic
▶ a story focusing on the properties of materials.

Science skills

The activities included in this chapter encourage the children to develop a variety of skills, such as observing, questioning, describing, sorting, sequencing, finding out, listening, speaking, reading, writing and drawing. For example, sorting objects according to the materials from which they are made will help foster children's observational skills, while describing how they found out which materials were waterproof will encourage speaking and listening skills. Children's natural curiosity can be encouraged by questions, such as *How can we find out? What would happen if…? Why do you think…?* At this stage children may need help in formulating initial questions but will soon be full of ideas once an enquiry is underway.

NOTES ON THE CD-ROM RESOURCES

Modern house

This photograph of a modern house shows clearly some of the building materials that are used in the construction of homes today. The walls are made of brick and the roof is tiled. Tiles may be made from clay or even, in some cases, plastic. The drainpipes and guttering are plastic, as will be much of the internal plumbing. The doors and window frames are wood although UPVC (a type of plastic) may be used in some modern homes. Glass has been used for the windows. Ideally, use this photograph in conjunction with a trip out of the classroom where the children can look at buildings. You can use this photograph to remind children about the variety of materials used in modern buildings on your return.

Discussing the photograph

▶ Discuss what the walls of the house in the photograph are made from and why bricks have been used. Remind them that bricks are strong and can easily be made from clay.
▶ Talk about how the bricks are fixed together to make the walls.
▶ Ask the children if they can tell you what the guttering and drainpipes are made from. Discuss why so many things in the house will be made from plastic. (Because it is an easily shaped, strong and waterproof material.)
▶ Ask the children if they can tell you what the windows are made from. Why do they think they have been made from glass?
▶ Look again at the photograph and ask the children if they can identify any other materials used, such as wood.
▶ Discuss what the roof is made from. Ask, *Why do we need a roof? What is important about the material we choose for the roof? Why are the tiles overlapping each other?*
▶ Ask why the children think we need drainpipes and what would happen if there was no guttering or drainpipes. Prompt their thinking by asking, *Where does the water go? What are the pipes made from?*

Activities

▶ Take the children outside and let them look at some brick walls. Focus on the patterns made by the bricks. Are they all the same? Get the children to make rubbings to take back to the classroom.
▶ Give the children plastic bricks and ask them to try and copy the patterns they saw on the walls, or on the walls of the house in the photograph. Ask the children why they think the bricks are built up in patterns. Would the wall be as strong if the bricks were just piled one on top of each other? Do the children think the plastic bricks are as strong as the brick walls?
▶ Make a roof shape from bent card and pour water over it. Ask the children to observe how the water runs off but soaks the card. Cover a similar piece of card with plastic and repeat the investigation. Make sure the children notice how the water runs off and doesn't soak the card, keeping the 'roof' dry.
▶ Use the 'Materials word cards' on photocopiable page 41 for the children to make labels from and attach them to an enlarged copy of the photograph to show the materials used.
▶ Encourage the children to learn 'The house that Jack built' (photocopiable page 48) to get them used to the materials used in modern building.

Old house

This photograph of an old cottage shows walls made of stone and a thatched roof. It shows building materials that were used for centuries, and are still used, but less so than in the past. They are usually more expensive than the modern materials generally used for house building today. This photograph can be used to compare the materials used in building in the past with modern construction through the picture of the 'Modern house' (provided on the CD).

Discussing the photograph

▶ Ask the children to look at the photograph and describe the building they see. Explain that it is called a cottage. How can they tell it is an old house?
▶ Ask if anyone in the class, or anyone they know, lives in a cottage.

▶ Can anyone suggest what the walls are made from? Discuss why stone is a good material to use for walls. Ask, *How are the stones stuck together? Is there a pattern?* Talk about how stone was found locally when these houses were built. Tell the children that before motorised transport, moving heavy loads was a long, laborious process, so houses were often built of local materials.

▶ Ask the children what the roof is made from. Explain what a thatched roof is made from if they do not know. Thatch could be either reed or straw depending on availability. Bundles of reed or straw are used to make a thick covering on a roof. Both of these materials are good at repelling rain water and because of their long, thin shape, they encourage the water to run down and off the roof on to the ground. Thatch is also a very good insulator, helping to keep the house warm.

▶ Can the children tell you why there is no guttering around the thatched roof? (Because the thatch is so thick that the rain water runs off it well clear of the walls and does not run down the walls and make them damp.)

▶ Talk about the fact that plastic was not discovered until the early 20th century, so pipes were made of metal before this time. Explain that lead was available and easy to work with, so that was often used for pipework. Tell the children that people were unaware at that time that lead is very poisonous, and it isn't used in plumbing today.

▶ Ask the children to look particularly at the windows. What do they notice? Point out that windows were often much smaller in the past than those found on a modern house because of the expense of glass and because smaller windows don't let in the cold as much.

Activities

▶ Give the children copies of photocopiable page 41 and let them use the word cards to make labels to attach to the photograph to show the materials used to build the cottage.

▶ Help the children to adapt 'The house that Jack built' (photocopiable page 48) to reflect the cottage by substituting the materials with those shown in the photograph.

▶ Show the children the photograph of the cottage with the photograph of the 'Modern house' (provided on the CD) and ask how many differences they can see between the two.

▶ Ask the children to write about the windows of both houses. How are they different in each photograph? Why do they think this is? What similarities can the children note?

Different houses

This picture illustrates the variety of materials used in building. It shows (from the left) a stone cottage with thatched roof, a stone house with a slate roof and a modern house made from brick and tiles. Children may be used to the buildings in their area being constructed from very similar materials. Old calendars can be a good source of pictures of older buildings if you live in an area where buildings are mostly made of brick. Even where buildings are made of similar materials (bricks, for example), there may be examples of brickwork in different colours, or it may be laid in a different pattern. Stone may be rough or dressed or, these days, cut very squarely by machine.

Discussing the illustration

▶ Ask the children how many different buildings they can see in the illustration.

▶ Can the children tell from the picture which buildings are old and which are more modern? Ask them what they have based their judgements on. Is it on the materials used?

▶ Ask the children to compare the different types of buildings and to talk about what they are made from.

▶ Talk about the different properties of the materials and why one might be better than another for a particular purpose.

▶ Ask what the children notice about the panes of glass in the windows of the houses. Why do they think the modern house has bigger panes of glass in its windows?

Activities

▶ Make a list on the board of all the different materials used in the buildings in the illustration.

▶ Ask the children to use collage materials to make a picture of their own house. Put these together to make a street. Some children could add a shop or two, and a church or public building.

▶ Read 'The sad story of the three little pigs' (photocopiable page 46) with the children and discuss the suitability of the materials they chose.
▶ Get the children to make models of the three little pigs' houses using appropriate materials.

Winter clothes

This photograph shows a child dressed for cold, wintry weather. The children should know that the materials from which the clothes are made are important and have been chosen for their insulating properties, such as the woollen scarf and gloves. Some materials may be chosen because they are waterproof and, therefore, help to keep us dry as well.

Discussing the photograph
▶ If you are doing this unit in the winter, ask the children what extra clothes they wore to come to school today. If it is summer, ask if they can remember what sort of clothes they wore last winter.
▶ Encourage the children to think about why we wear so many more clothes in cold weather than when it is warm. Ask, *Why do we need gloves and woolly hats or scarves?*
▶ Talk about why boots might be useful in the winter. Ask the children what the essential properties of the materials from which they are made are. Can they think why we wear raincoats or carry umbrellas?

Activities
▶ Let the children carry out a simple test to find the best material for a good raincoat or rain hat. Put a small plastic animal in a jar and fix various materials over the top with an elastic band. Make sure you have a good range of materials, including waterproof and non-waterproof ones. Show the children how to test each material by pouring water over the jar. If the animal gets wet then the material is not waterproof!
▶ Fill two or three hot water bottles with warm water. 'Dress' one bottle in a T-shirt, one in a cardigan or jumper and one in a thick warm coat or anorak. Let the children feel the bottles at 30-minute intervals to find out which material keeps the bottles warm for the longest time.

WOODEN OBJECTS

Breadboard, Table, Spoon, Chair

These photographs show a collection of wooden objects to show the children that different objects, with different uses, can be made from the same material. The properties of wood enable it to be easily shaped and joined. It is strong, but can also be decorative. It has many uses in building and domestic situations.

Discussing the photographs
▶ Show the children each photograph and ask them if they can name any of the objects.
▶ Can they tell you what material the objects are all made from?
▶ Can they tell you where wood comes from? Talk about the fact that trees are the largest plants on earth.
▶ Tell the children that wood is a material that can be used in a number of ways and that it is a material that people have always used. As well as being cut and shaped fairly easily, it can be carved, smoothed and polished to make both useful and beautiful things. It has also been used for thousands of years as a fuel for fires, for keeping warm as well as for cooking purposes.
▶ Discuss the properties that make wood a suitable material for making each of the objects in the photographs. For example, the wood can be shaped to make all the objects. It is strong enough to support someone when they sit on the chair. The spoon can be used to stir hot liquids without the handle getting hot. The breadboard is a suitable surface for cutting on.

Activities
▶ Make a list on a flip chart or board of all the wooden things found in the classroom.
▶ Take the children on a walk around the school and list all the things made from wood in the local environment. Add this to the list on the flip chart and talk about why the things that they have found have been made from wood and not from another material.

▶ Make a collection of wooden objects and let the children handle them and describe how they feel. Get them to focus on what they are used for. Are some objects useful and some for decoration? Encourage the children to bring wooden objects from home to add to the collection.
▶ Choose words together from the 'Properties word cards' on photocopiable pages 42 and 43 that describe the material. Use them to add to the display of wooden things.

METAL OBJECTS

Saucepans, Dustbin, Key, Spoon

These photographs show the children the diversity of objects that can be made from metal. It is not necessary at this stage for children to be able to name individual metals. They should know that metals can be very strong and can be formed or moulded into many useful objects. Some children may have noticed that metal objects can get very hot. This is because one of the properties of most metals is that they are good conductors of heat. At this stage children need to form the concept that metal is attracted to a magnet. However, not all metals are attracted to a magnet, only those that contain iron. If you are asking children to sort materials with a magnet, make sure that at first, all the metal objects they are given are magnetic. Understanding that not all metals are magnetic is the next stage in the development of the concept.

Discussing the photographs
▶ Show the children each photograph and ask them to identify the objects in the pictures.
▶ Can anyone tell you what the material used to make all the objects is?
▶ Can the children tell you about some of the properties of metal? Why do they think that it has been used to make the objects in the photographs? For example, metal is very strong and durable. It has been formed to make the saucepans, which can withstand the heat of a cooker without being damaged. Metal heats up very quickly, which speeds up the cooking process.
▶ Discuss why metal is a suitable material for making many things that we use every day, ranging from tiny things like a press stud or an earring to enormous things like giant oil tankers and jumbo jets. Explain to the children that it is strong and relatively easy to mould by heating it until it is runny. Tell them that it can be made rigid or flexible, and that it can be joined in a number of ways. It can also be made dull or shiny, given a patterned surface, and so on.
▶ Can the children name any other things made from metal?

Activities
▶ Make a collection of metal objects and allow the children to handle them, describe how they feel and say what they are like. For example, rigid, flexible, strong, and so on. Ask the children to relate this to why metal has been chosen to make the objects in the collection.
▶ Let the children choose words from the 'Properties word cards' on photocopiable pages 42 and 43 to add to the collection of metal objects. Add any additional words that the children come up with.
▶ Ask the children to compare the metal objects with the collection of wooden objects (or compare the photographs from the CD). Do they think any of the objects could be made from either metal or wood, for example a spoon? Can they tell you when it would be best to use one or the other because of its properties? For example, a wooden spoon is better than a metal one for stirring hot things because it does not get hot, and a metal fork with a wooden handle is best for turning food on a barbecue because the metal does not burn.
▶ Give the children copies of the 'Comparing properties word cards' on photocopiable pages 44 and 45 and ask them to write statements using the words to compare the properties of the objects in the metal and wooden collections.
▶ Put the collection of wooden objects and the metal objects that are magnetic together and ask the children to separate them using magnets.
▶ Make a fishing game. Let each child decorate a small fish shape and fix a paperclip to it. Show them how to make a simple rod from dowel, string and a small horseshoe or circular magnet. The children can then take turns to try and 'catch' a fish, the paperclips being attracted to the magnet.

PLASTIC OBJECTS

Watering can, Spoon, Hat, Spade

It would seem that almost everything in today's world is made from plastic. Children may have some difficulty in distinguishing some plastic imitations of wood, for example, from the real thing. The objects in these photographs are all recognisably plastic.

Discussing the photographs

▶ Show the children each photograph and talk about the variety of objects shown. Can the children tell you anything about the material from which they are made?

▶ Discuss the properties of plastic that make it a good choice for making the objects in the photographs. Some children may realise that not all plastic is the same, that some is hard and rigid while some is soft and flexible, and still other types can be made very thin and used for plastic bags. Make sure they realise it may be coloured or clear, transparent or opaque.

Activities

▶ Make a collection of plastic things found in the classroom. Ask the children to bring in objects made from plastic to add to the display.

▶ Get the children to make labels from the 'Properties word cards' provided on photocopiable pages 42 and 43 to add to the display.

▶ Ask the children to sort the objects in the display into different sorts of plastic. For example, rigid, bendy, opaque, transparent.

▶ Put out a variety of materials, such as small pieces of plastic, wood, paper, tinfoil and fabric, and ask the children to sort the plastic from the rest.

▶ Make a class collage of a river or lake with brightly coloured fish and dragonflies using plastic materials, such as clear plastic sheeting, coloured plastic bags, packing material, coloured plastic straws, beads, buttons, and so on.

CLAY OBJECTS

Brick, Mug, Vase, Plant pot

Clay is an interesting material in that if it is allowed to dry it becomes hard and brittle but if it is soaked it will return to its former plasticity. However, if the dried clay is fired at high temperature then the change is not reversible. This is a concept children will come to later, but they need to understand, at this stage, that the material has undergone some profound changes between the soft clay that they may have handled to make models with, and a hard cup they use to drink from.

Discussing the photographs

▶ Ask the children to name the objects in the photographs. Can they tell you what they are all made from?

▶ Why do the children think the objects in the photographs have been made from clay? Most of the objects in the photographs could be made from other materials, but clay is relatively inexpensive and easily shaped. Clay objects can be porous and useful for such things as plant pots, but can be made waterproof by glazing or firing at a higher temperature like the vase.

▶ Can the children think of any other objects that are made from the same material?

▶ Pass round some pieces of raw clay for the children to feel and handle. Talk about how it feels. Then pass round an object made from fired clay, such as a plant pot or mug. Discuss the differences between the finished object and the raw clay.

▶ Some children may be familiar with working with clay themselves and making simple objects. Ask them to remember what it felt like and what they had to do to shape the material when it was in its raw form. If the clay was fired, ask if they can remember how it changed.

Activities

▶ Give the children copies of the 'Properties word cards' on photocopiable pages 42 and 43 and ask them to choose appropriate words to add to the display.

▶ Get the children to write sentences using the 'Comparing properties word cards' on photocopiable pages 44 and 45 to compare the clay, glass, metal and wooden objects.

▶ Look around the school together for objects made from clay. Draw the children's attention to such things as wash basins and lavatory bowls that they may miss.

▶ Let the children use pottery clay to make a small object that can be dried and fired if possible.

GLASS OBJECTS

Tumbler, Beads, Window, Bottle

Glass is a fascinating material that children will be familiar with but may not have handled very much because of its brittleness and the dangers associated with broken glass. Objects like paperweights or small solid ornaments are less likely to shatter and are safer for the children to handle under supervision. These photographs show the versatility of this material.

Discussing the photographs

▶ Ask the children if they can tell you what material the objects in the photographs are made from and what each of the objects are.

▶ Can they tell you anything about the properties of glass? Have any of them had experience of the sharpness of broken glass?

▶ Ask the children why they think that glass is such a useful material. Discuss the fact that glass is often transparent, enabling us to see what is inside a jar or bottle. Explain that because glass is easy to clean it makes it good to use with food, and that because it is waterproof it is very good for storing liquids. Talk about how because glass is so breakable plastic is often used instead for things like bottles and bowls.

▶ Can the children suggest why glass is used for windows?

Activities

▶ Use the word cards on photocopiable pages 42 and 43 and ask the children to find words that describe the properties of glass. Can they think of any more? Make a list of any additional words the children suggest and ask them to use the full collection of words to write a short poem describing glass.

▶ Ask the children to note, in pictures or words, all the things they use at home that are made from glass.

▶ Walk to a local church if possible to look at stained glass windows.

▶ Use coloured cellophane or acetates for the children to make 'stained glass windows'.

Waterproof clothes

This photograph shows how we use the waterproof property of some materials to keep us dry and comfortable when in wet conditions. The children should be able to relate to both the clothing in the photograph and the fun activity that the children in it are doing.

Discussing the photograph

▶ Discuss with the children what is happening in the photograph. Ask them what is special about the children's coats and footwear. (Point them towards the clue of the watering can if they are struggling.)

▶ Discuss the meaning of the word *waterproof* and ask the children why they think wearing waterproof clothing, like that in the photograph, is a good idea when it is raining.

▶ Why do the children think it is a good idea to wear wellingtons when it is wet?

▶ Ask the children to think of some other uses of waterproof materials, such as the waterproof outside of babies' nappies, tents and groundsheets, armbands for swimming in, or the plastic bags that are used to carry shopping home.

Activities

▶ Make a class list, in pictures or words, of people who need to wear waterproof clothing in their work, such as firefighters, fishermen, police officers.

▶ Put a collection of waterproof and non-waterproof materials in the water tray for the children to explore.

▶ Get the children to carry out a simple test to find the best material for an umbrella. Let them use a range of waterproof and non-waterproof materials and ask them to predict which materials they think will be waterproof before they carry out the test.

NOTES ON THE PHOTOCOPIABLE PAGES

Word cards PAGE 41

These word cards contain some of the basic vocabulary for the children to use when learning about sorting and using materials. They include:
▶ words relating to materials
▶ words relating to the properties of materials
▶ words to compare the properties of materials.
Read through the word cards with the children to familiarise them with the key words of the unit. Ask which words the children have heard before. Are there any words they don't understand?

Activities
▶ Cut out and spread the word cards on the table and ask the children to find specific words.
▶ Cut out the 'Properties word cards' and the 'Comparing properties word cards' and ask the children to sort them into pairs of opposites, such as *hard* and *soft*, *shinier* and *duller*.
▶ Let the children add the words to the alphabetical lists in their personal dictionaries.

The sad story of the three little pigs PAGE 46

This story has been retold to emphasise the materials used by the three pigs to build their houses.

Discussing the story
▶ Read the story with the children and invite them to join in all the huffs and puffs that the wolf does.
▶ Discuss each of the pigs' choice of materials to build their houses from with the children. For example, the straw would be cheap and readily available in the countryside but not very strong. The wood would also be cheap and readily available and would be stronger than straw but not as strong as the bricks, and so on.

Activities
▶ Let the children make models of the three little pigs' houses out of appropriate materials. They could use a construction kit to make the house of bricks.
▶ Turn the story into a simple play for the children to act out.
▶ Ask the children to look carefully at their own house and to draw or collage a picture of it, showing the materials that it is made from. They can add labels to their pictures with the names of the materials on them.

The house that Jack built PAGE 48

This is a play on the traditional nursery rhyme using the materials used in building a modern house.

Discussing the text
▶ Read the rhyme to the children and talk about the various materials mentioned in it.
▶ Get the children to listen to the rhythm of the poem and to join in the repetitions.

Activities
▶ Show the children the photographs of the 'Modern house' and the 'Old house' (provided on the CD). Can they tell you whether they think the house in the rhyme is an old one or a new one? How can they tell?
▶ What different materials would be in the rhyme if the house were an old one?
▶ Help the children to adapt the rhyme so that it is about an old house, by substituting the appropriate materials.

Materials word cards

metal

wood

plastic

paper

glass

clay

Properties word cards (1)

hard

soft

rough

smooth

shiny

dull

Properties word cards (2)

magnetic

transparent

opaque

bendy

waterproof

strong

harder

softer

rougher

smoother

shinier

duller

bendier

stronger

the same as

different from

READY RESOURCES ▶▶ S C I E N C E

The sad story of the three little pigs

Once upon a time there were three little pigs, Eenie,
Meenie and Mo. They lived with their mother in
a nice warm sty.

One day their mother said, "Now you three, you
are getting to the age when you ought to be
making your own way in the world. Off you go."

Eenie, Meenie and Mo decided that they would
each build a house so that they could live in a grand
style. *They* didn't want to be sty pigs for the rest of
their lives.

So Eenie, being the eldest, set off to build a house for
himself.

"Mind you, watch out for the Big Bad Wolf," said their mother. "He likes
nothing better than a good pig dinner."

Eenie set off to find a good spot and some suitable material from which to
build his house. He hadn't been walking for long before he saw a farmer
stacking sheaves of wheat straw in his field. "I could build a house of
straw," thought Eenie.

The farmer was quite happy to let him have enough straw for a
house, and to let him build it in a sheltered corner of the field.
"Straw will make a lovely warm house," said the farmer,
"and if you bind the straw together tightly on the roof it
will be waterproof, like a thatched roof. I have my doubts
about the house being strong enough, though."

Eenie took no notice and worked hard all day
building a house of straw. He was very pleased
with it.

As soon as he had shut the door the Big Bad Wolf
came wandering through the field looking for
dinner – preferably a nice plump pig! When he came
to the straw house he could smell pig and got very excited. He knocked on
the door. Eenie looked out of the window, remembering that his mother had
said he should be careful. When he saw the wolf he hid under the table and
stayed very quiet. The wolf shouted in his fiercest voice:

"Little pig, little pig, let me come in, or I'll huff and I'll puff and I'll blow
your house in."

Eenie stayed under the table, shivering with fear.

The wolf waited a while and when he heard nothing he filled his lungs with
as much air as he could, and he huffed and he puffed with all his might. The
straw house fell down. And the wolf ate Eenie for his dinner.

The next day Meenie set off to make his way in the world. He saw a man in the woods cutting and piling up sticks. The man kindly gave him enough sticks for a house, but told Meenie that sticks were not a very strong material to build a house with, especially in a gale of wind. Meenie took no notice and built a smart house of sticks.

That evening the wolf strolled through the woods and came upon the stick house. He could smell a strong smell of little pig. He knocked on the door and shouted:

"Little pig, little pig, let me come in, or I'll huff and I'll puff and I'll blow your house in."

Meenie hid under the bed. When there was no answer the wolf filled up his lungs and blew. The house shook, but didn't fall down. The wolf tried again and this time the house wobbled and fell down. Of course, the same thing happened to Meenie as had happened to Eenie.

When Mo heard about what had happened to his brothers, he thought hard. "The straw house and the stick house were not strong enough," he said to himself. "I shall have to think of some other material for my house."

Then he had a good idea. The sty was made of bricks. It was very strong and they had always been safe there, so he would build his house of bricks.

That is what he did. When the wolf came along he knocked. Getting no answer he huffed and puffed as usual. Nothing happened. Then he huffed and puffed again. Again nothing happened. He huffed and puffed and huffed and puffed, but the brick house was too strong. In the end the wolf sat down exhausted and angry.

Then he noticed the chimney on the roof. It looked big enough for a wolf to get down. "I'll go down the chimney and gobble him up," thought the wolf. "What a clever plan!"

He began to climb up the drainpipe and across the roof. Mo heard him coming. Being a clever little pig he too had a plan. He put a huge pot of boiling water on the fire at the bottom of the chimney and as the wolf fell down, Mo took off the lid and the wolf fell into the boiling water.

So that was the end of the Big Bad Wolf. And if you ever find that strong brick house you will see that there are happy pigs living in it to this very day!

Photographs © Photodisk

The house that Jack built

This is the house that Jack built.

These are the bricks that made up the walls that went in the house that Jack built.

These are the doors that kept out the draught that went in the walls that made up the house that Jack built.

These are the windows made of glass that let in the light and went in the walls that made up the house that Jack built.

These are the tiles that went on the roof that sat on the walls, the windows and doors, that went in the house that Jack built.

This is the chimney that topped off the roof that sat on the walls, the windows and doors, that went in the house that Jack built.

Photograph © Ikon Imaging

LIGHT AND DARK

Content and skills

This chapter links to Unit 1D 'Light and dark' of the QCA Scheme of Work for science at Key Stage 1. The Light and Dark Resource Gallery on the CD-ROM, together with the teacher's notes and photocopiable pages in this chapter, can be used when teaching this unit.

As with the QCA Scheme of Work, this chapter looks at comparing light and dark and identifying sources of light. It also helps children to understand that we use light sources in a variety of ways in everyday life. Light is often an important part of religious festivals as well as giving pleasure at such events as firework or laser displays.

Resources on the CD-ROM

The resources include pictures of different light sources, such as a table lamp, a torch, car headlights and warning lights on an emergency vehicle. These photographs show that lights can be used in different ways. There is a photograph of someone wearing reflective strips on their clothing in order to help keep them safe. Photographs of fireworks, candles and fairy lights enable the children to learn about light sources used for pleasure and in a religious capacity. There is a video clip showing how shadows are formed by the Sun on a bright sunny day but are absent when the sun is hidden by cloud.

The accompanying teacher's notes contain background information and include ways of using the resources as a whole class, for group work or as individuals. Some of the activities suggested will link with other areas of the curriculum, such as English, maths or art. Wherever possible the activities encourage the children to ask questions and develop an enquiring approach to their learning.

Photocopiable pages

The photocopiable pages in the book are also provided in PDF format on the CD-ROM and can be printed out from there. They include:
▶ word cards containing the essential vocabulary for the topic
▶ a poem.

Science skills

Skills such as observing, questioning, describing, sorting, sequencing, finding out, listening, speaking, reading, writing and drawing can be drawn out of the children during the activities provided in the teacher's notes. Asking questions and listening to the ideas of others will help to develop questioning, speaking and listening skills, as will joining in discussions about any of the resources. Sorting light sources from things that are merely reflective will encourage observation and sorting skills. Taking various objects into a dark box to see if they reflect light will help to foster investigative skills.

NOTES ON THE CD-ROM RESOURCES

LIGHT SOURCES

Lamp, Torch, Headlights, Candles, Warning light, Sun

The photographs in this section aim to teach the children that all light comes from a light source. The photograph of the Sun can be used to focus on the fact that this is our main light source. (Be sure to explain to the children that the moon is not a light source as it only reflects light from the sun, but that stars (really far away suns) are light sources as they produce their own light.) The other photographs can be used to show the children that when there is little or no natural light from the Sun we use other light sources, such as candles, electric lights and torches. At this stage in their learning children often think that that when the Sun goes behind a cloud it causes night to fall, so challenge this idea if you have children who think this.

Discussing the photographs

▶ Ask the children if they know what a light source is. Help them to understand that a light source actually gives out light. Explain that some things, such as mirrors, are shiny, but that these things only reflect light, they are not light sources.

▶ Show the children the photographs. Discuss with them the fact that all the things in the pictures are sources of light. Can they name each object and say where they might find it or how they might use it?

▶ Discuss why the Sun is such an important light source. Talk about how it is the Sun that gives us light and heat, and that without it nothing would be able to live on the Earth.

▶ Remind the children that it is dangerous to look directly at the Sun because it can seriously damage our eyes.

▶ Ask the children why we need light. Can they do things as easily in the dark as they can in the light? Does it matter how bright the light is? Talk about how a low light level is fine if we are relaxing, but that we need a brighter light for seeing to do detailed work.

▶ Discuss when and why we use different lights, for example for reading or for lighting our way home on a dark night. Talk about how some lights warn us of danger, such as the flashing light on a police car or ambulance, or on a lorry reversing. Show the children the appropriate photographs when discussing these uses.

▶ Ask the children to think of as many warning lights as they can. Ask, *Do these always warn us of danger?* Talk about the difference between warning lights on a police car and the small lights, such as those on a TV or video, that warn us that a piece of equipment is switched on or working.

▶ Always make sure that the children are well supervised when observing candles and that candles are in a stable holder placed on a bed of sand in a metal tray. Ask the children to suggest their own safety rules, for example tie long hair back, always sit at a safe distance from the burning candle.

▶ Ask the children to think about what it would be like if there were no lights in the street or at home. Have they ever experienced a power cut? What did they do?

Activities

▶ Ask the children to name the light sources in each of the photographs. Record these on a board or flip chart and ask the children to think of more sources of light. Add these to the list.

▶ Look around the classroom for any sources that have not already been mentioned, such as the light that shows that the computer or the television is switched on.

▶ Encourage the children to look about them at school and at home for the next few days and see if they can identify any further light sources. Add these to the list.

▶ The children could draw or paint pictures of a street scene with as many warning lights in it as they can think of.

▶ Play Blindfold Buff with the children and ask them why they cannot see with a blindfold on. This will help them to understand that we need light in order to see things.

▶ Reading *The Owl Who Was Afraid of the Dark* by Jill Tomlinson (Egmont Books) with the children would be a very good accompaniment to the teaching of this unit.

▶ Use the poem 'A dark, dark house' (photocopiable page 58) with the children to read for fun.

Reflective

The horse and rider shown in this photograph are both wearing reflective strips that show up in the dark. It is important that children learn the difference between things that are light sources and that give out light, and things that merely reflect light. Since it is often difficult to find a really dark place in the classroom, a dark box would be useful when teaching children about this. Paint the inside of a large cardboard box with matt black paint. If you can get a very large box that a child can actually get into, so much the better.

Discussing the photograph

▶ Ask the children to look carefully at the picture and tell you what it shows.

▶ Discuss why people wear reflective strips on their clothing. Talk about how the strips reflect light to show that someone is there when it is dark, and that this is important so that they can be seen. Ask the children to think about people such as crossing patrols, firefighters and police officers who wear reflective strips on their clothes so that people can see them in the dark. Talk about how the strips help to keep them safe.

▶ Ask the children if they have any reflective strips on their clothing. If so, when do they wear them? Ask the children if they have ever seen any other children wearing reflective strips to keep them safe?

▶ Can the children tell you when or where reflectors could be useful for keeping people safe other than on clothing? For example, on a bicycle or other vehicles, such as police cars; on the paddles that the person waves to direct an aircraft into place for unloading its passengers; on boats at anchor in a harbour.

▶ Ask the children if reflective strips can be seen clearly in the daytime? Talk about how things can be seen more clearly in the daylight so there is no need for the strips, but at night the reflective strips show up even if there is only a small amount of light.

www.eyecatchers.com

Activities

▶ Ask the children to help you make a list of all the people who might wear reflective strips on their clothes to help keep them safe.

▶ Ask the children to choose one of the suggestions and to paint the figures and stick reflective strips on their clothes.

▶ Put out a selection of materials including examples of reflective, non-reflective, matt and shiny things. Ask the children to sort out the shiny things. Do they think that these objects will shine in the dark? Take these things into a dark room or dark box where there is no light at all. Can they still see them? Discuss with the children that, as shiny things are not light sources, they can't be seen in the dark. Take them into the dark box again with a torch. Can they see them now? Why?

▶ Ask the children to sort the reflective materials into a group. Do they think these things can be seen in the dark? Ask them to check whether they are right by taking the materials into a dark box and finding out. Do they still need a light source in order to see them?

FESTIVE LIGHTS

Fireworks, Christmas lights

Use these photographs to show the children that we sometimes use lights for pleasure and celebration, and that they are often used at particular times of the year.

Discussing the photographs
▶ Talk about the fact that most cultures and religions have festivals and celebrations during which they use lights.
▶ Ask the children to look at the photographs and tell you what sort of celebration each might be involved in.
▶ Ask them whether they have ever been to any celebrations where lights were used? Can they tell you about them? Do they have lights on their Christmas tree or candles on a birthday cake?
▶ Talk about other festivals where lights are used. Many religious festivals include lights, such as Christmas or Divali. Some give us pleasure, such as birthday candles or fireworks on bonfire night or at New Year.
▶ Can the children tell you whether all the lights they have mentioned as being festival or celebration lights are also light sources?
▶ Can the children tell you why bonfire and firework parties take place in the dark? Would they still be able to see the lights as well in the daytime? Help the children to understand that the light from the Sun in the daytime is so bright that other lights do not show up well.

Activities
▶ Ask the children to use the words on the word cards on photocopiable page 56 to help them to write exciting 'light word' poems. Words such as *lantern*, *candle* and *Sun* should help them.
▶ Let the children paint pictures using pastels or chalks on black paper, or make collages with glitter, to represent festivals with lights.
▶ Invite members of the community to come into school and talk to the children about festivals and celebrations they have that include light.

Video: Landscape showing shadows

The video is a time-lapse sequence showing clouds moving across the sky. The shadows can be seen moving across the fields in the background as the Sun is obscured by the clouds. Because the cloud cover is not complete, the shadows made by trees on the river bank are always visible, but become much sharper when the Sun is not behind cloud. Make sure that the children recognise the difference between the shadows and the reflection of the trees in the water.

Discussing the video
▶ Ask the children where the light in the video is coming from. What is the light source? Reinforce the earlier discussion about the Sun and the dangers of looking directly at it.
▶ Explain to the children that this piece of film is speeded up so that everything seems to happen very quickly. Look at the video again. Ask, *Why does it sometimes go dark?* Ask the children to watch the sky in the clip. Can they see the clouds going by? Can they explain why it goes dark when there are lots of clouds? Discuss the formation of shadows and how a shadow is formed if something gets in the way of the light. When the Sun is shining the trees get in the way and form shadows. When the clouds pass in front of the Sun they form a great big shadow.
▶ Discuss the fact that the Sun going behind the clouds does not cause night. As the Sun goes behind a cloud it may get a little darker, but as the Sun reappears it becomes brighter again. Make sure that the children understand that this is different from night-time when it is really dark and the Sun does not appear again until the morning.

Activities
▶ Take the children outside on a sunny day but when there is some cloud and wind so that the clouds are moving fairly quickly across the sky. Remind the children never to look directly at the Sun. Watch the shadows appear and disappear as the Sun goes behind the clouds. Ask the children to tell you what is happening and why sometimes there are shadows and

sometimes not. Reinforce earlier discussions, if appropriate, about how this is different from night.

▶ Make a class collage divided into cloudy and sunny sections, putting in shadows on the sunny side but leaving them out when the Sun is behind the clouds.

▶ Ask the children to run about on the playground on a sunny day. Can they run away from their shadows? Ask them to try and catch each other's shadows. Can they make their shadows link arms or shake hands?

NOTES ON THE PHOTOCOPIABLE PAGES

Word cards 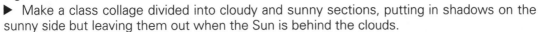 PAGE 54

These word cards contain some of the basic vocabulary for the children to use when learning about light and dark. They include:

▶ words related to light and dark, such as *bright*, *black*, *night*
▶ words related to light sources, such as *candle*, *Sun*, *lantern*
▶ words to compare light and dark, such as *darkest*, *brighter*.

Read through the words with the children and explain any words they don't understand.

Activities

▶ Use the words as the basis for a class word bank, adding any others during the course of teaching this unit.

▶ The children can use the word cards to help them in labelling pictures or to help them with their writing.

The dark, dark, house 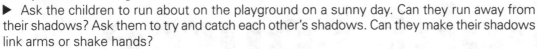 PAGE 58

This is a fun poem that most children enjoy. They soon learn to join in. Start off in a very quiet voice and get louder and louder towards the end until the ghost appears with a shout. Children need to know that dark is the absence of light.

Discussing the text

▶ Read the poem through with the children and talk about why the house is so dark. (Because there is no light.) Ask, *Do you think anyone still lives there? Why aren't the lights working?*

▶ Ask the children why they think we say the first part of the poem so quietly and then shout at the end?

▶ Talk about the fact that there is really no need to be afraid of the dark. Dark just means that there is no light but everything around us, for example in our bedrooms, is the same in the light or the dark. Talk about how we sometimes enjoy feeling frightened, such as riding on a roller coaster or climbing a wall.

Activities

▶ Encourage the children to learn the poem and let them enjoy reading it.

▶ Act out the poem with the children creeping through the house in the first part of the poem and then showing surprise or fright at the end.

▶ Make a collection of smallish boxes, such as shoeboxes with a well-fitting lid, for the children to make their own dark box. Ask the children to paint the inside of the box black and help them to make a small hole in the lid of the box and one in the side of the box. Show them how to cover the hole in the lid of the box with black insulating tape. Then get them to make a ghost shape from white paper, put it in the box and close the lid. Ask them to peep into the hole in the side of the box. Can the ghost be seen? Suggest they take the tape off the hole in the lid of the box and shine a small torch through it. Ask them to peep into the hole in the side of the box again. Now can the ghost be seen? This activity is fun but will also help the children to understand that we cannot see things unless there is light.

Light and dark word cards (1)

light source

bright

light

dark

black

Light and dark word cards (2)

night

day

reflect

reflective strip

Sun

torch

candle

lantern

headlights

warning light

Comparing light and dark word cards

lighter

lightest

darker

darkest

brighter

brightest

The dark, dark house

In a dark, dark wood
There's a dark, dark house.
In the dark, dark house
There's a dark, dark room.
In the dark, dark room
There's a dark, dark cupboard.
In the dark, dark cupboard
There's a GHOST!

PUSHES AND PULLS

Content and skills

This chapter links to unit 1E 'Pushes and pulls' of the QCA Scheme of Work for science at Key Stage 1. The Pushes and Pulls Resource Gallery on the CD-ROM, together with the teacher's notes and photocopiable pages in this chapter, can be used in teaching this unit.

As with the QCA Scheme of Work, this chapter looks at different sorts of movement and relates these to simple science in terms of pushes and pulls, speed or direction, and starting things moving as well as stopping them. Children also need to begin to understand the possible dangers to themselves from moving objects, for example around the area of road safety.

Resources on the CD-ROM

There is an illustration of playground objects that are moved in various ways by children pulling or pushing them. A picture of a wind farm shows how moving air or wind is a force that can move things. A picture of children blowing bubbles shows this on a smaller scale. The traffic video enables children to discuss safety in relation to moving objects.

© Gleaston Water Mill, Cumbria www.watermill.co.uk

The teacher's notes in the accompanying book contain background information and suggest ways to use the resources when teaching the children. These notes include ways of using the resources as a whole class, for group work or as individuals. Some of the activities suggested will link with other areas of the curriculum such as English, maths or art. Wherever possible the activities encourage the children to ask questions and develop an enquiring approach to their learning.

Photocopiable pages

The photocopiable pages in the book are also provided in PDF format on the CD-ROM and can be printed from there. They include:
▶ word cards containing the essential vocabulary of the topic
▶ an informative text on animal movement
▶ writing and drawing frames.

Science skills

The activities in the teacher's notes require the children to draw upon a variety of skills, such as observing, questioning, describing, sorting, sequencing, finding out, listening, speaking, reading, writing and drawing. For example, joining in a discussion about the apparatus found in the illustration of the playground and how they move will help to foster speaking and listening skills as well as an understanding of simple forces.

NOTES ON THE CD-ROM RESOURCES

Playground

This illustration shows young children playing on moving equipment. At this stage in their learning, children sometimes think that moving just means moving from place to place. This picture can help children to learn that moving also means that objects can be made to move, speed up, slow down and change direction.

Discussing the illustration

Ask the children to look carefully at the picture and to tell you the names of all the equipment they can see in it.

▶ Discuss which piece they like playing on best and why.

▶ Ask the children if they can tell you how each piece of equipment works and what is making it move. Help them to describe the movement of each piece of equipment. Ask, *Is it being moved by a push or a pull? What about the equipment that doesn't move – are forces such as pushes and pulls still involved?* (For example, pushing the feet against the rungs of the climbing frame or the ladder on the slide to get to the top.)

▶ Discuss with the children what they need to do to make each piece of equipment speed up or slow down. Ask them how this relates to forces. For example, to make the horse on a spring move, they need to push their bodies forwards and then pull them backwards. To make the horse speed up they need to do this harder and faster.

▶ Ask if the children think the direction of any of the equipment in the picture could be changed by a push or a pull? For example, the swings can be pushed forward or pulled back.

Activities

▶ Give enlarged copies of the illustration to individuals or groups and ask them to use the word cards provided on pages 65 and 66 to help them label the equipment in terms of how it moves. They should consider if an item is pushed, pulled or twisted (the latter is a combination of a push and a pull).

▶ Ask the children to name some other objects that can be moved by pushing or pulling. For example, a shopping trolley, roller skates, bicycles or pull-along toys. Can they say whether a pull or a push is needed for each? Make lists on a board under the headings *Pull* and *Push*.

▶ Can the children think of any objects whose direction they could change by a push or a pull? For example, batting a ball is using the push of a bat to change the direction in which the ball is travelling. Let the children practise changing the direction of objects using small PE apparatus.

▶ Link a PE session with the word cards on photocopiable pages 65 and 66. Ask the children to move in ways suggested by the words – they could spin, jump or twist. Then ask the children to draw pictures of themselves moving in different ways. They could then label their pictures using copies of the word cards.

▶ Read the poem 'He pulled, we pushed' by Michael Rosen from *Centrally Heated Knickers* (Puffin Books) with the children to reinforce the notions of pushing and pulling.

▶ Ask the children to think of an animal and to draw a picture of it moving. Then get them to write a sentence about how it is moving and whether it using a push or a pull. For example, *The kangaroo is pushing its feet on the ground to help it jump*, *The bird is using its wings to pull itself through the air* or *The cat is using its claws to pull itself up the tree*. Use the texts 'How animals move' (photocopiable page 69) or 'Animal movement' (photocopiable page 70) alongside the children's drawings.

▶ Ask the children if they can think of any animals that use their bodies to push and pull to help us to move things. For example, horses pulling carts, elephants moving logs, donkeys or camels carrying loads.

Wind farm

Children may think that it is only animals that can make things move by pushing or pulling them. They need to understand that things such as wind and water are powerful forces and can also cause movement. At this stage children sometimes think that it is the trees that cause the wind by waving their branches, rather than the other way round. They need to be

encouraged to think and ask questions about what is causing any movement of objects, such as the wind turbine in the photograph.

Discussing the photograph
▶ Talk with the children about the fact that it is not just animals that can make things move by pushing or pulling them.
▶ After looking carefully at the photograph, ask the children to tell you what they think makes the wind turbine turn.
▶ Ask the children to tell you what happens to the wind turbines when the wind blows. Ask them what happens to their hair and their clothes when the wind blows? Is it easy to walk into the wind or do they have to push against it?
▶ Discuss the fact that wind is moving air. Explain that it can't be seen, but it can make things move. We know it is there even though we can't see it because we can feel it and see what it does to other objects.

Activities
▶ Take the children out on a windy day to observe the effect of the wind and to feel it on themselves.
▶ Let the children make carrier bag 'kites' by giving each child a plastic carrier bag and showing them how to tie a length of string to one handle. Take them out on a windy day and try flying them so that the children can feel the wind pulling them. (Make sure that the children are well supervised, understand the safety rules about carrier bags and do not put them over their heads.)
▶ Ask the children to draw pictures of themselves on a very windy day. If you are doing this in the autumn, children could add fallen leaves to their pictures, showing them blowing in the air and on the ground.
▶ Experiment with the effect of moving air by letting the children play blow football with drinking straws and either ping-pong balls or screwed-up pieces of paper.
▶ Show the children how to make moving-air pictures, by dropping runny paint onto paper and using a straw to blow it into windy shapes.
▶ Read *Mrs Mopple's Washing Line* by Anita Hewett (Red Fox) or 'Wind Force' by Michael Rosen from *Centrally Heated Knickers* (Puffin Books) with the children.

Water wheel

The wheel is a marvellous invention that makes things easier to move by helping to overcome the force of friction. Wheels on simple carts moved by humans or animals have been used for centuries to move loads. Nowadays, they are often powered by engines using various fuels and children will be familiar with wheels on cars, buses, lorries and trains. This photograph of a water wheel will help children to learn that wheels can also be powered by such things as wind or water.

The photograph is of an undershot mill wheel. The wheel is moved by water flowing under it and catching and pushing on the overlapping wooden slats. Overshot water wheels are moved by the water falling into little 'buckets' from above to push the wheel round.

Discussing the photograph
▶ Discuss with the children the fact that wheels help us to move things more easily. Ask, *How easy would it be to push a pram that had no wheels? Would their roller skates work without wheels?*
▶ Ask the children to describe what is happening in the photograph. Ask, *How is the wheel moving? What is making it move?*
▶ Talk about the different ways in which wheels can be made to turn, such as humans or animals pushing or pulling them, wind and water moving them, and so on. You could also introduce the way they can be moved by using fuel in a motor.
▶ Ask the children if they can think of any wheels that are moved in other ways. For example, in clockwork toys, pull-back toys, battery driven motors or a hamster turning a wheel in its cage. Again, ask *What is causing these wheels to move?*
▶ Talk about wheels that go round but do not travel along, such as a hamster wheel, a toy windmill or a roundabout. Ask the children if the wheel in the photograph travels or just goes round.

Activities

▶ Give the children a task, lasting several days, during which they are to observe as many different types of wheels as they can that are made to move in different ways. For example, wheels moved by humans, such as prams, shopping trolleys, roller skates, bicycles; wheels moved by fuel in a motor, such as cars, motorbikes, trains. Depending on the area you are in, children may see others, such as windmills, water wheels, and so on. Each child could use a copy of 'Wheels' (photocopiable page 71) to help them note the type of wheel they see and to list how it works.

▶ Make a collection of as many different-sized circles or round things as you can and ask the children to print a wheel picture using them. They could add such things as spokes, valves and hubs to make their circles more wheel-like.

▶ Allow the children to play with dry sand and water, using both materials to turn a toy water wheel. Discuss what is happening and what is making the wheel turn.

Blowing bubbles

When bubbles are blown children are creating their own 'wind' in order to form the bubble and set it free from the bubble blower. Any breeze will then move it about and carry it away. This photograph shows children blowing bubbles of varying sizes and how the bubbles are created by the wind formed by the children's breath. Some children may not have had the experience of blowing bubbles through a blower, so make sure that they all know how to use one before you begin the session. This avoids mess and upset! Bubble blowing is best carried out outside if possible, or in a well-ventilated place. Some asthmatic children may react to the soap or detergent molecules in the air if you blow bubbles in a confined space. Make sure the children do not rub their eyes with soapy fingers or blow bubbles into each other's faces.

Discussing the photograph

▶ Ask the children to tell you what is happening in the photograph.

▶ Can anyone explain how the children in the photograph are making the bubbles? Explain how their breath is acting like the wind and moving the 'skin' on the bubble blower and pushing on it, causing the bubble to form and float away.

Activities

▶ Get the children to blow their own bubbles, preferably outside on a slightly breezy day when the bubbles are likely to blow about nicely. (A solution of good quality washing-up liquid and water makes a very suitable bubble mixture. Unfortunately, eco-friendly mixtures do not work for bubble blowing! It may be necessary to experiment in advance with the strength of the solution.) Talk about what is happening as the children blow on the soapy skin and after the bubbles have separated from the blower. Who can blow the biggest bubble?

▶ Let the children make bubble prints, by adding washing-up liquid to a paint/water mixture, making a froth on the top by blowing through a straw (make sure the children don't suck by mistake!) and laying sheets of paper on the surface.

Video: Traffic and road safety

This video shows traffic moving on a busy street. It can be used to reinforce both the learning about road safety and how wheels make things move.

The importance of children understanding the need for road safety and taking great care when they are out, and when they are crossing, cannot be overestimated. Children sometimes learn the rules parrot-fashion and then forget to apply them in a real situation. Even if they know about keeping themselves safe, and understand the need to be careful and follow the rules, children often do not realise that vehicles take time to stop. This session can be linked with work on the senses to reinforce children's understanding that our senses help to keep us safe and that we need to use them when crossing the road.

Discussing the video

▶ Before watching the video, ask the children what they know about how to keep themselves safe when they are out and about.

▶ Do any of them have to cross a busy road on the way to school? Where do they cross? Do they have anyone to help them?

▶ Do they know how to cross the road safely? Ask them to tell you what they would do. This will give you a good idea of the depth of their knowledge and understanding and help you to build on it.

▶ Play the traffic video. Talk about the amount of traffic on the road.

▶ Ask the children if they think all the vehicles are travelling (moving) at the same speed. How can they tell? Talk about the importance of watching carefully to assess the speed of approaching vehicles and also of listening hard. Explain that the sound of an engine may also give a clue as to the speed.

▶ Play the video again and talk about how the traffic slows down before it stops. Ask the children what the driver has to do to stop the car. Explain that the brakes rub against the wheels to make them slow down and stop. Remind the children that cars and lorries cannot stop immediately, and the faster they are going the longer it will take them to stop, especially in wet or icy weather. Tell the children that they should never run out in front of moving traffic and should always use a pedestrian crossing if there is one.

▶ Watch the people crossing the road. Tell the children it is only safe to cross when the lights change to red for the cars, and even then they should keep looking left and right. If there is a green man to show the pedestrians when to cross safely, they should wait for him to appear.

Activities

▶ Ask the children to point to the parts of themselves that can help to keep them safe when they are crossing the road, or anywhere where there is traffic. Link this with work on the senses. For example, ask *How do our ears and eyes help to keep us safe?*

▶ Use the word cards on photocopiable page 68 to familiarise the children with the key words around traffic safety, such as *stop*, *listen*, *be careful*.

▶ Reinforce how cars and lorries take time to come to a stop by using the words on photocopiable page 67, such as *go faster*, *go slower*, to talk about how vehicles move.

▶ Make class posters about road safety rules that would help other children to keep safe.

▶ Ask the school-crossing patrol people to come in and talk about how they help to keep the children safe from the traffic as they come to school and go home. Ask the children why they are sometimes called the *lollypop lady* or *man*?

▶ Make a large picture or collage of the school-crossing patrol person and ask the children to write a few words about how they help to keep us safe. Perhaps the patrol person would lie down, in their uniform, on a big sheet of paper so that the children can draw round them to start off their picture!

▶ Take the children outside to a safe vantage point and survey the traffic. Get them to think about if there is always the same amount of traffic. Are there any parked cars?

▶ As the children are watching the traffic, reinforce the road safety rules that the children have learned. Ask them to tell you about any other dangers they can think of and how they could keep themselves safe.

▶ Back in the classroom talk about, and make a list of, the dangers mentioned by the children and add anything that they have not talked about. For example, they should never cross the road without an adult; crossing between parked cars is dangerous because the oncoming traffic can't see them; they should never cross the road if they can see or hear a car coming because they can't tell what speed it is doing and it might not be able to stop in time.

▶ Chalk a 'road' on the playground. Include a pedestrian crossing, traffic lights and parked cars. Ask the children to practice what they have learned using this 'road'. If you have wheeled playground toys or vehicles, they can be used to make the situation more real. Ask a child to role-play being the patrol person so that others can cross the road safely.

NOTES ON THE PHOTOCOPIABLE PAGES

Word cards   PAGE 65

These word cards contain some of the basic vocabulary for the children to use and learn when learning about pushes and pulls. They include:

▶ words related to movement, such as *spin*, *push* and *pull*

▶ words related to comparisons of movement, such as *go faster*, *go slower*

▶ words related to safety, such as *danger*, *look*, *listen*.

Read through the word cards regularly with the children, explaining any words they don't understand initially.

Activities
▶ Spread the cards on the table and ask the children to find specific words by talking about their context or providing them with a definition.
▶ Use the word cards as a word bank to help the children label pictures or to help them with their writing.
▶ Let the children use the word cards to help them make a caption for a poster about road safety.

How animals move   PAGE 69

This is a simple information sheet that the children can use to help them understand which parts of their bodies animals use to push or pull themselves along.

Discussing the text
▶ Read the sentences through with the children and discuss each one, clarifying anything the children don't understand.
▶ Talk about which parts of their bodies animals usually use to move themselves. For example, many animals use four legs; humans use two, but they also use their arms if they are running or swimming; birds use their wings.
▶ Discuss how animals without legs move. For example, fish use their tails and fins, snakes slither along using muscles under their skin, and snails have strong muscles in their 'foot' with which they can pull themselves along.

Activities
▶ Watch a snail moving over a sheet of clear plastic. Look for the muscle rippling in the foot as the snail pulls itself along.
▶ Play the children the video of 'Animals moving' provided in the Living Things Resource Gallery on the CD-ROM.
▶ In PE ask the children to work in pairs. Get one child to move while the other watches carefully to see which parts of their bodies they use when moving. Which parts are pulling and which parts are pushing?
▶ The children can use the information on the sheet as a basis for making a booklet about how animals move by pushing or pulling.

Animal movement   PAGE 70

This is a sheet for the children to complete to help them focus on how animals move. They could use it after watching the video about 'Animals moving' in the Living Things Resource Gallery on the CD-ROM, after observing animals in the local environment, or alongside the use of secondary sources when finding out about an animal.

Wheels   PAGE 71

This sheet helps the children understand that wheels help us to move things, but that they need a force to move them. It could be used as an observation sheet to use at the school gate for a short time or taken home to be completed as homework. Read the sheet with the children and make sure they understand what they have to do.

Movement word cards (1)

twist

spin

swing

slide

swerve

hop

Movement word cards (2)

jump

turn

fast

slow

push

pull

Comparison word cards

go faster

go slower

go further

Safety word cards

safe

danger

be careful

look

listen

stop

◣ SCHOLASTIC
PHOTOCOPIABLE

How animals move

Humans use their legs to walk, run, skip, hop and jump by pushing against the ground.

Four-legged animals use all four legs in the same way.

Some animals use their limbs to pull against trees or fences to help them climb.

Birds and flying insects use their wings to pull themselves through the air.

Fish use their fins and tails to push and pull themselves through the water.

Animal movement

Draw a picture of an animal and complete the sentence. Use the words in the boxes to help you.

This is my animal.

It is a _____

It moves by using its _____ to _____

itself _____

| legs | wings | claws | fins | tail | | push | pull |

| along the ground | through the water |
| through the air | up a tree |

Wheels

Write how the wheels are used. Use the words at the bottom of the page to help you.

	How they move		How they move

Other wheels I saw	How they moved

human   engine   animal   wind   water   battery

SOUND AND HEARING

Content and skills

This chapter links to unit 1F 'Sound and hearing' of the QCA Scheme of Work for science at Key Stage 1. The Sound and Hearing Resource Gallery on the CD-ROM, together with the teacher's notes and photocopiable pages in this chapter, can be used in teaching this unit.

As with the QCA Scheme of Work, this chapter looks at exploring a variety of sounds and how they are made. Children are encouraged to identify familiar sounds and consider how listening is important in road safety.

Resources on the CD-ROM

There are photographs of individual musical instruments and a picture of a full orchestra playing. An extract from an orchestral work where individual instruments can be heard will allow children to match pictures to sounds. A selection of familiar sounds, such as a baby crying, provides a flexible aural resource to use with the children.

Teacher's notes containing background information and suggesting ways in which to use the resources in teaching are provided here. These include ways of using the resources as a whole class, for group work or for individual use. Some of the activities suggested will link with other areas of the curriculum, such as English, maths, art or music. Wherever possible the activities encourage the children to ask questions and develop an enquiring approach to their learning.

Photocopiable pages

The photocopiable pages in the book are also provided in PDF format on the CD-ROM and can be printed out from there. They include:
▶ word cards containing the essential vocabulary of the topic
▶ a specially written story focusing on sound effects

Science skills

The children will need to use skills such as observing, questioning, describing, sorting, sequencing, finding out, listening, speaking, reading, writing and drawing when taking part in the activities provided in the teacher's notes and when using the resources on the CD-ROM. For example, from looking at the picture of the orchestra, children can see that musical instruments are played in different ways. This could act as a stimulus for them to explore designing and making their own instrument. It will also support them when listening to the musical extract and enable them to describe the instruments they can hear with greater detail.

NOTES ON THE CD-ROM RESOURCES

MUSICAL INSTRUMENTS

Drum, Violin, Trumpet, Flute, Cymbals, Didgeridoo, Sitar

Children need to understand that musical instruments are played in different ways and that they can produce very different sounds. They may be familiar with percussion instruments, but many may be unfamiliar with wind or string instruments, depending on their cultural background. Music is vitally important to all people and provides an excellent way for children to learn something of other cultures.

Drums of some kind are used by people throughout the world. The drums in this photograph are of the kind used in the western world and may be very like some of the drums in the school collection. The violin may be familiar to the children and some members of the class may be learning to play it. The trumpet is a wind instrument used in all types of music, from classical orchestras to brass and jazz bands. The photograph clearly shows the valves that can be used to alter the length of the tube to change the notes. The flutes in the photograph are from South America and made from cane, not metal like western flutes. The cymbals are being played by Tibetan monks as part of a religious ceremony. Again, the children may be familiar with a smaller version of these from the school music trolley. The didgeridoo is a traditional Australian Aboriginal instrument made from a hollow log. Unlike many instruments it has no mouthpiece and is quite difficult to get a note from! The sitar comes from the Indian sub-continent. It is a string instrument with a distinctive tone. It is played by plucking, whereas the violin is usually played by bowing.

Discussing the photographs

▶ Look at each of the photographs in turn. You may wish to start with instruments with which you think your children might be most familiar.

▶ Print the photographs out and place them on a table. Ask the children to name as many of the instruments as they can. Ask, *Which instrument would you expect to see in a concert orchestra?*

▶ Discuss what each of the instruments are made from. For example, the metal cymbals or the wooden digeridoo.

▶ Can the children tell you from which country some of the instruments originate?

▶ Talk about how each instrument is played. Ask, *Do you need sticks or bows, or do you just use hands and fingers? Do you have to blow?*

▶ Ask the children if any of them play an instrument of any kind. Ask them to talk about how long they have been playing it and whether they have special lessons.

Activities

▶ Ask the children to sort the pictures into groups according to how the instrument is played.

▶ Encourage the children to use picture books to find more instruments. Which groups would they fit these instruments into?

▶ Use the school instruments and ask the children to group them according to how they are played. Then get them to add the photographs to these groups.

▶ Hide a child plus instrument behind a screen and ask the rest of the class to guess which instrument is being played and to say how it is played.

▶ In groups, ask the children to make a simple instrument from reclaimed materials. Then let them join together as a class and use the instruments to make a simple tune.

▶ Ask the children to use their bodies, including their voices, to make as many different sounds as they can. For example, clapping, stamping, whispering, singing, humming, slapping thighs, clicking fingers, and so on. Can they make an interesting sound sequence using the different sounds?

▶ Record some of the sound sequences and play them back to the whole class. Can the children tell how any of the sounds are being made?

▶ Ask the children each to choose an instrument from the school collection, make a detailed observational drawing of it, and label it as to what it is made from and how it is played. They could use the word cards on photocopiable page 77 to label their drawings, using words such as *pluck* or *shake*.

The orchestra and Orchestral music

Many children of this age will never have seen a full orchestra playing. They may have heard music played by an orchestra without appreciating how many instruments were involved. The photograph shows part of an orchestra and how instruments of the same kind are grouped together. It gives some idea of the number of people who can form a full orchestra, and the instruments involved. The musical extract supports what the children can see in the photograph, as most of the instrument groups can be heard in it.

Discussing the photograph and the music
▶ Ask if any of the children have ever been to see an orchestra or band. Can they describe the experience to the rest of the class?
▶ How many different instruments can they see in the photograph? Is there more than one of each kind? Can they see the conductor? What does he do?
▶ Ask the children if they think the photograph shows the full orchestra. Can they tell you what other instruments might be part of an orchestra?
▶ Can the children tell you why the instruments are grouped together and not scattered about? For example, each group of instruments makes a concerted sound and the conductor can gesture to each group when he wants a particular response.
▶ Play the 'Orchestral music' to the class. Discuss with the children which instruments they can hear. Can they hear the violins? Ask them to put up their hands when they hear the drums. Can they see the violins and drums in the photograph? Can they hear any other instruments playing?
▶ Do the children think that all the instruments are playing all the time? How do the musicians know when to play? For example, by following the music and watching the conductor.

Activities
▶ Give the children a copy of 'The orchestra' photograph and play the music again. Can they point out the instruments they can hear on their photograph and say how they are played?
▶ Let the children use the word cards on photocopiable page 77 to add labels to their photograph, describing how each instrument is played, such as *blow*.
▶ Play the piece of music and get the children to look at the photograph again. Discuss how the instruments combine to make the sound of the orchestra.
▶ Invite a musician or group of musicians into school to play for the children and encourage the children to discuss their various instruments with them.
▶ Begin each day by sitting the children on the carpet to listen carefully to a short piece of orchestral music. Try and provide music of different moods and discuss with the children how the music makes them feel. Which instruments can they hear?
▶ While listening to music, ask the children to move according to the mood of the music and the way it makes them feel.

FAMILIAR SOUNDS

Owl, Doorbell, Vacuum cleaner, Baby crying, Lorry reversing

These audio clips contain familiar sounds for the children to identify. Children need to know that they hear sounds by listening with their ears. These sensitive organs send messages to the brain so that sounds can be distinguished. They need to know that their sense of hearing helps them to make sense of the world around them, and that being able to identify warning sounds can help to keep them safe.

Discussing the sounds
▶ Before playing the sounds, ask the children to think about how they use their ears in everyday life.
▶ What sounds have they noticed hearing already today? Did they have the radio or television on before coming to school, or did they listen to a CD? Whose voices have they heard? Did they hear any animals or traffic sounds on the way to school?
▶ Play the clips of familiar sounds to the children. Ask them which part of their bodies they used to listen to the sounds.
▶ Can the children identify each sound and tell you where they might have heard it before?

▶ Discuss with the children how our hearing helps to keep us safe. For example, listening for traffic when crossing the road. Can the children tell you which of the 'Familiar sounds' might be warning people of something?

Activities

▶ Go on a 'listening walk' with the children and make a list of all the sounds you hear. Back in the classroom, can the children suggest any groups they could be sorted into, such as happy, sad, warning sounds, and so on?

▶ Stop the class at intervals during the day and ask them what they can hear. Is there ever complete silence?

▶ Can the children think of any warning sounds? For example, an emergency vehicle siren or the bleeps at a pedestrian crossing. Make a list on the board of their suggestions. Ask them why they think warning sounds are important.

▶ Give the children a copy of 'Jay's birthday' (photocopiable page 79) and read it with them. Encourage them to use percussion instruments or different materials to make their own sound effects to accompany this story.

▶ Groups of children could record their own selection of sounds for the rest of the class to guess what they are, or how they were made.

NOTES ON THE PHOTOCOPIABLE PAGES

Word cards
PAGE 76

These word cards contain some of the basic vocabulary for the children to use and learn when learning about sound and hearing. They include:

▶ words related to describing sounds, such as *rattle*, *blow*, *loud*, *soft*

▶ words related to making comparisons when discussing sounds, such as *louder* and *quieter*. Read through the words regularly with the children to familiarise them with the key vocabulary of this topic. On the initial read through, ask which words the children have heard before and check if there are any words they don't understand.

Activities

▶ Copy several sets of the word cards and let the children play word snap with them.

▶ Hold up one of the word cards from photocopiable page 77, such as *shake*, *rattle*, *pluck*, and ask the children to mime the appropriate action. Can they tell you which instrument they are pretending to play?

▶ Get the children to hum a familiar tune. Hold up each of the word cards from photocopiable page 78 in turn, such as *louder*, *quieter*, and ask the children to respond appropriately.

Jay's birthday
PAGE 79

This is a story about a small boy waiting for the postman to come on his birthday, and how he uses his sense of hearing to find out what is happening while he waits for his cards to arrive. The story illustrates the wide range of information that can be picked up by using our hearing.

Discussing the story

▶ Tell the children that you are going to read them a story and that they should listen very carefully to discover the sounds that the little boy in the story hears. For example, the door squeaking loudly as he goes out of his bedroom; the quiet sound as he whispers to himself.

▶ Read the story right through while the children just listen. Read the story again and ask the children to put up their hands every time a sound is mentioned.

▶ Discuss with the children what they could use to make each sound effect.

Activities

▶ Use the word cards on photocopiable page 76 to help the children focus on the type of sounds that the story contains. For example, *silence*, *quiet*.

▶ Read the story again with the children, letting them create the sound effects you discussed previously.

▶ Ask the children to make up their own stories with sound effects.

Describing sound word cards (1)

high

low

loud

quiet

soft

silence

Describing sound word cards (2)

shake

pluck

rattle

ring

blow

bang

Comparing sounds word cards

louder

quieter

further away

nearer

Jay's birthday

It was only just getting light when Jay woke up. He lay curled up under his duvet listening to the early morning sounds. Then he remembered – it was his birthday! Today he was six! He sat up quickly and thought about what he was going to do. He was having a party with some of his friends from school, but that wasn't until teatime. There must be something else before that. Then he remembered that Mum and Dad had said that he might get some birthday cards through the post. That meant that the postman would be bringing them.

Jay knew that the postman usually came quite early. Perhaps he had already been! Very quietly, Jay got out of bed and tiptoed to his bedroom door. He trod on the squeaky floorboard and stopped for a moment to make sure no one else had heard it. Slowly he opened his bedroom door. It always squeaked when he didn't want it to!

Carefully, he crept down the stairs to the front door. There were no letters on the mat yet. He decided to sit on the bottom step and wait for the postman. He gave a big sigh. "It might be a long wait," he whispered to himself, "but as I don't have a birthday every day it will be worth it."

Jay had only been sitting there for a short time when he heard someone whistling. Was that the postman? Jay couldn't remember whether he whistled or not. He heard footsteps crunching up the gravel path to the front door. He got up from the bottom stair ready to catch his cards as they fell through the letterbox. But he heard the clink of milk bottles as the whistling milkman put two pints on the doorstep and collected the empty bottles. He heard the footsteps crunch their way back down the path. He could hear the sound of the empty bottles being put into the crates and then the funny whirring noise of the milk float going off up the street.

Everything was very quiet and Jay was thinking about going back to bed when he heard the deep rumble of an engine. He didn't think the postman came in a lorry, but you never could tell. The sound of the engine changed as the vehicle stopped outside his house. Jay jumped up ready to catch the letters as they came through the letterbox. He heard lots of bumping and banging and men shouting to each other. It was the dustbin men, not the postman after all. Disappointed, he sat down on the bottom stair and listened to the clank of the bins being emptied into the back of the lorry. Then the bang as the bins were dropped back onto the pavement.

Again there was silence. No sounds came from either inside or outside the house. It was getting lighter outside. Jay yawned a great big yawn. He was beginning to feel quite sleepy when a sudden rattle of the letterbox made Jay jump. The postman! At last! The flap of the letterbox started to lift. Something started to come through. Was it a birthday card? Was it?

Something fell with a plop on the doormat. It was the newspaper! He heard the paper boy's footsteps crunching down the path and he began to think that the postman wasn't going to come. Today of all days! Jay's eyes began to droop and he curled up at the bottom of the stairs.

He woke up with a start and for a moment he couldn't remember where he was. He wasn't in his bed, but his duvet was wrapped round him. It was much lighter now and the sun was shining through the little window in the front door. He could hear someone humming in the kitchen. Then he heard the kettle boiling and that little click as it switched itself off. He could smell toast and he heard the toast pop out of the toaster. Then he remembered where he was and why he had got up so early. He must have fallen asleep at the bottom of the stairs. His Mum must have found him and covered him up rather than disturb him.

Just then he heard more footsteps crunching up the path. This time when the letterbox rattled lots of envelopes dropped onto the mat and spread out on the floor. The footsteps crunched back down the path. "It's my birthday and my cards have come!" yelled Jay, bouncing into the kitchen.

"Happy birthday," said his Mum. "I thought you were going to sleep there all day. Come and sit down and let's see what you've got."